Wow... an incredible read. Mentally ill people can be difficult patients. Mentally ill criminals - even more so. So what made a Glasgow woman spend her life trying to reach, treat and rehabilitate these most demanding patients? In this touching and honest account of life as a forensic psychiatrist, Rhona Morrison relates hilarious and shocking anecdotes, shines a light on to society's wrong assumptions and bravely anchors her life story in the personal traumas that beset her sister and husband. This is a fluent, compelling and intimate book about our disregard for folk living with mental illness and a clarion call for NHS professionals to show more empathy and take more time with patients on the margins.

>   – Lesley Riddoch, award-winning journalist,
>   broadcaster and author

I loved every page of I Don't Talk to Dead Bodies. It's emotional, amusing, shocking and best of all shared from the heart by the delightful and effervescent Rhona Morrison.

>   – Michael Heppell, Sunday Times no. 1 bestselling
>   author

This book offers an incredible insight into the world of a forensic psychiatrist, with bizarre, humorous and scary anecdotes. Most importantly, it challenges the reader to question their assumptions and the stigma surrounding mental illness. Highly recommended.

>   – Charlie Lawson, national director, BNI UK & Ireland

I DON'T TALK TO DEAD BODIES

The curious encounters of a forensic psychiatrist

DR RHONA MORRISON

I Don't Talk to Dead Bodies
ISBN 978-1-912300-78-5
eISBN 978-1-912300-79-2

Published in 2022 by Right Book Press
Printed in the UK

Contents

In memory of Dad, my Good Samaritan; Vivienne,
my stealth bomber; and Richard, my rock.
And for my greatest achievements, Jill and Fraser.

Prologue

'I don't talk to dead bodies!'

A ripple of laughter moves through the audience as I explain, yet again, that a forensic psychiatrist works with mentally ill criminals – not corpses in the autopsy lab. Actually I did complete a diploma in forensic medicine since so many patients and professionals expected some knowledge about bodies and crime scenes. But the image of a psychiatrist talking to a corpse is a million miles from the reality of my working life.

Not everyone is suited to a career in forensic psychiatry. You need to be able to look beyond the offence and the newspaper headlines and see the person, hear their story and identify whether or not mental illness is a causal factor. You must be able to remain non-judgemental and respect the person, even when they've raped a child or murdered a pensioner. Mental illness sometimes makes good people behave badly. My job was to find them, treat them and rehabilitate them. Some might say, 'Why bother? Just lock them up and throw away the key.' But I wonder if those people would have the same opinion if a relative of theirs developed a mental illness and offended because of it? Then they might say, 'It wasn't them; it was the illness that made them do it.' I suspect they'd want them to be treated and rehabilitated. The importance of valuing a person for who they are is deep rooted in me and stems from my weekly childhood visits to my sister, Vivienne, who had learning disability, physical disability and sensory impairment. She shaped my core values, my career choice and how I relate to others.

Having retired after 32 years in the NHS, I've had a chance to reflect on the highlights, the challenges, the inspirational people and bizarre encounters along the way. Life experiences are like pieces of a jigsaw that come together to make us who we are. Being born in a castle, learning what's important in life from my silent sister, meeting my husband in a gay bar in Belgium, associating with rapists and murderers, serving a 'life sentence' in a female prison, coping with a stalker, becoming a full-time carer and navigating bereavement – all these events played their part in shaping who I've become.

Unless they're already in the public domain, all of the stories in this book that relate to patients have been altered or amalgamated in order to anonymise them and protect patient confidentiality. I've used them to illustrate the types of encounters I had during my career, and to highlight the wonderful individuals I met who were learning to live with illness. If you're a former patient or colleague of mine and think you recognise a snippet of your personal story in this book, please know that you were an important part of my journey, and it was a privilege to be part of yours. This is my story, as I remember it.

CHAPTER 1

My Secret Garden

While I was a pupil at Kirkintilloch High School, I wrote an essay titled 'My Secret Garden'. My friends wrote about money trees and secret gates to wonderful lands, but I wrote about my brain, with its intricate intertwining pathways and blooming ideas. As you can see, my creative, lateral thinking came to the fore at an early age. When I got my essay back, there were five different grades along the top of my jotter. It had been passed round the whole department and they'd all given a view. I suppose the content was a little out of the ordinary for a 12-year-old, and probably an early indication of my future career path.

Later on, when I consulted my careers advisor, it became apparent that psychiatry, psychology or mental health nursing were all in contention for me. Daunted but not deterred by the prospect of at least 13 years of study ahead, I opted for medicine, planning to specialise in psychiatry and then sub-specialise in learning disability psychiatry. The alternative was for me to apply to Glasgow School of Art, as art was my best subject and passion, but I was told I should take a more academic path and keep art as a hobby. So, why specialise in psychiatry? To answer that I need to wind back a little further. I could romanticise the situation, saying that Kathryn and John Pollock had just brought a little princess into the world (after all, she was born in a castle), but the reality was somewhat different. I was daughter number three. Fingers crossed I'd be all right because daughter number two was not. It was brave of my parents to try for another baby, not knowing what the future would hold for Vivienne. Luckily for me, I'd arrived unscathed. As for the castle, it was Lennox Castle Hospital. There was indeed an actual castle there, but I was delivered with no pomp or ceremony in the maternity ward situated in its grounds, on 23 March 1963. This would go on to become a significant date beyond being my birthday, a sort of bookmark for my life.

Some experiences and people have a profound impact on us, but we don't always recognise it at the time. Vivienne was my stealth bomber. She got under my radar and shaped my future path. She was two-and-a-half years older than me, making me the youngest. Elaine was the eldest by five years. Vivienne looked perfect when she was born, but after being starved of oxygen at birth she became a 'floppy baby' who never cried. After she developed a rash and was hospitalised, it became clear to my parents that something was wrong. She failed to achieve the normal milestones and at 18 months they were told, 'She's deaf, dumb and blind, mentally and physically handicapped. She's going to need 24-hour hospital care.' She was admitted to Waverley Park Home in Kirkintilloch, and my family moved from Glasgow to be nearer to her. It's difficult to comprehend, but they never knew if she knew who they were. Auntie Lizzie visited religiously midweek, and our family visited every weekend.

My memories of attending Waverley Park as a young child include a large cot bed with metal bars on the side and squeezing my hand between them to hold Vivienne's hand. There were pretty murals of nursery rhyme scenes on the wall, and other patients would wander past and talk to me. When I was out with my mum, I would sometimes meet the patients at a local shop, and they seemed happy enough. Vivienne used to giggle and smile too. She was always lying on her side under the covers. I later learnt that her bones were brittle and if she hit her arms on the sides of the cot, she was prone to fractures. The covers kept her from waving her hands around, but the result was that she developed muscle contractures from lying in the foetal position, so she grew into that shape. It was a logistical challenge trying to source soft, stretchy clothes that would accommodate her Z-shaped body. I was good at spotting them in shops and took my role as family present-buyer seriously. It was important for her to look nice. The problem with her bones seemed to resolve itself and, as I became physically stronger, I was able to take my turn lifting her out of the cot bed and onto my knee. She loved being bounced up and down and would 'goo' and 'gaa' excitedly, smiling from ear to ear. She responded to Dad's voice, and he became adept at making her laugh, with raspberry noises and 'giddy giddy giddy'. She could clearly hear something, so I became a mimic. I loved making her smile. We had a strong bond, and I think she also enjoyed my chocolate button treats. I felt closer to her than anyone else in the family. My parents were always supportive but not emotionally demonstrative people. I cuddled Vivienne. Even now, it's hard to put our relationship into words.

In her early teens, Vivienne was transferred to Lennox Castle Hospital, which was a much bigger institution. We were told she had to be moved when she started to menstruate, but the logic of this escaped me. Due to her physical, sensory and learning disabilities, her inability to sit up or walk and her incontinence and epilepsy, she was placed in the hospital wing, where she could receive 24-hour nursing care. I enjoyed my weekly visits, and when it wasn't my turn to have Vivvie on my knee, I spent time with the other patients, trying to encourage a new word or a smile and hearing from the more able patients what they'd been up to during the week. The seed was sown. I got so much personal satisfaction from helping others that I knew I wanted to pursue a career in a caring profession.

It's funny how your own experience can be so far removed from the reality of a situation occurring only a few feet away, in another part of a building. I later read an article in *The Scotsman* under the headline 'The Sad Secrets of Glasgow's Mental Hospital'. It talked about Lennox Castle and how it had been built in the 1830s. It was converted into a hospital in the early 20th century, with the new mental deficiency institution opening in 1936. It was heralded as the largest and best-equipped hospital of its kind in Britain, with capacity for 1,200 patients. Unfortunately, due to overcrowding, understaffing and underfunding, the conditions for patients gradually deteriorated and were described as wretched and dehumanising. A study in the late eighties reported that a quarter of the patients were underweight and malnourished. There were also reports of physical cruelty, unnecessary medication being given to keep patients calm, incidents of non-accidental injury and even death. But that was not my experience of Vivienne's care. Despite all of this, an invisible umbilical cord had remained in place between me and Lennox Castle, pulling me back again and again. Not only was I born there and my sister Vivienne a patient, I also worked there as a nursing assistant during my summer holiday jobs while at university and, years later, went back on placement as a trainee forensic psychiatrist. The hospital closed in 2002 after the remaining patients were relocated to more modern facilities. A multitude of secrets had been hidden behind its lush, leafy driveway.

CHAPTER 2

Handshakes, Not Hugs

Because of Vivienne, I had a visceral reaction when I heard anyone use derogatory terms like 'spaz' or 'spastic', which were commonly used back in the seventies. One day, I heard a gaggle of teenagers snigger as one of them said, 'He's a right spaz.' I immediately shot back, 'I don't find that funny. My sister's mentally and physically handicapped.' I felt uncomfortable about the reaction I might get, but there was no doubt that I needed to say it. At that moment I became Vivienne's advocate. I never judged her; I just valued her for who she was. This was the age of *The Black and White Minstrel Show* and adults talking about going round to the Paki shop or ordering a Chinky (Chinese meal). These days it would be called politically incorrect. There was no discussion of equality and diversity, social inclusion or Black Lives Matter. In those days, racism and religious sectarianism were alive and kicking in the west of Scotland. We also had sectarian violence between the supporters of the two main football teams, Glasgow Rangers and Celtic, who were clearly identified as Protestant and Catholic adversaries. These issues were never really discussed in our end-terrace council house, partly because Dad was a teetotal

Church of Scotland elder who didn't watch football. However, I was still aware that turning up in a Celtic top wouldn't have been tolerated.

Mum always cooked from scratch, so we didn't have takeaway meals. She'd trained at 'Dough School' (Glasgow School of Cookery, later Queen's College) and became a school meals supervisor, but had to give that up when she got married – another sign of the times. I must confess to enjoying *The Black and White Minstrel Show*, but the fact that it featured white men wearing black face paint was lost on me. However, my parents bought me a black dolly and I was proud to own her. She looked different and I liked her for that. There were no children with physical disabilities or from ethnic minorities at my primary school until Khalid and Karmjot joined. Initially I thought they were exotic, with their unusual names and different-coloured skin, but then they became friends, just like everyone else. At the time, it never occurred to me what it must have been like for them, standing out in a sea of white faces.

Families had a specific way of conditioning their children where I grew up: 'You should be seen and not heard. Your mother and father know best. Clear your plate before you leave the table – there are children starving in Africa.' You learnt to do what you were told and not question anything. I was on the receiving end of parental messages linked in part to wartime rationing and in part to my mother having been served the same food at the next mealtime if she hadn't cleared her plate. I can only imagine facing a plate of reheated tripe. And when it came to expressing emotion, we were all reserved: 'Well done, congratulations' followed by a handshake. Or: 'Welcome home. Glad you're back safely. Did you have a good time?' Well, that's how I was brought up. That was my world, so I thought that was how it was in the world beyond our council house.

I can clearly recall the moment later in life when I was forced to question my version of reality. My dad was on stage in the church hall, constructing a magnificent Burns cottage for the Burns Night supper, with a thatched roof that had smoke coming out of the chimney. Later, I would be wearing a white shirt and tartan sash, doling out soup, haggis, neeps and tatties, followed by traditional oatcakes and cheese. Willie, who was helping with the construction process, approached me afterwards. To my horror, he entered my personal space, put his arms around my shoulders and pulled me towards him in a hug. I went rigid, my shoulders welded to my earlobes. What was this? It was new, uncomfortable, awkward.

The most significant challenge to my reserved upbringing came when I met my boyfriend Richard's parents for the first time back in 1980. I heard the crunch of gravel as we entered the driveway of their Mount Vernon home, as two smiling strangers approached, arms outstretched. They were ready for a warm embrace, not only for Richard but also for me. Feeling my shoulders on the rise again, I willed them to remain in place. I wondered what was wrong with my family. We didn't do hugs and kisses. Over the next few months, I became desensitised to the hugs and lived between the parallel universes of Kirkintilloch and Mount Vernon. I decided that if I ever had a family, I was going to learn this hug-and-kiss malarkey because it felt good. When Richard and I got engaged two years later, Mum and Dad shook my hand and made a cup of tea. They never realised how emotionally reserved our family was. It wasn't that we weren't loved, cherished and supported; it was simply that I'd been born into a 'handshakes, not hugs' culture. But I was open to change. Perhaps my ultimate choice of husband was more significant than I thought. Unconsciously, I chose someone born into a 'hugs and kisses' universe who didn't really 'do emotion' himself. He would hug and kiss, but otherwise wasn't particularly emotionally demonstrative. Richard was solid and reliable. He straddled the two universes, knitting them together to form our lasting bond.

Whenever I'm asked where I met Richard, I always answer,

'A gay bar in Belgium.' It always gets a reaction. Actually, we met 24 hours before that, when I stepped into the Waverley Badminton Club minibus to go on tour to Belgium. I'd been invited by Jan, my county ladies' doubles badminton partner. I didn't know anyone else and felt a bit awkward. The man driving the minibus had red hair and a moustache and didn't say much. I reckoned he was about 40 years old. When the drivers changed over, he came to sit across the central aisle from me, took out a crossword and started completing it. He didn't even acknowledge me. I wasn't impressed! After we arrived in Belgium, Jan and I agreed to share a room, and the group arranged to meet later for drinks. This was only my second visit to a pub, the first having been a few months earlier in Inverness when I played in the north of Scotland badminton tournament. They had sneaked me in, which felt quite risky for an underage girl who didn't usually break the rules, but I was only drinking Irn-Bru (Scotland's national non-alcoholic drink). There was a bearded Highlander in the bar with a cockerel that appeared to be doing tricks, holding a cigar in its beak and sipping whisky from his glass. Having no frame of reference, I thought, 'Pubs are quite interesting.'

In Belgium, the nearest bar was next to the hotel. This being my second visit to a bar, I felt a bit braver but was still underage. It was empty, so we piled coins into the jukebox, selected some songs and settled in. It was soon 10.45 pm. Suddenly, someone unplugged the jukebox before our songs had played. We complained that it wasn't 11 pm yet, but saw a band arriving and setting up in the corner. The man who had tried to spoil everything was now strapping on an accordion. We didn't have to leave after all, because the only requirement in Belgium was to close for one hour in every 24, so the bar began to fill up again. The situation started to become more intriguing for this naïve 16-year-old as men at the bar started to caress each other. A hand slipped under a shirt and a man appeared wearing a green silk dress, with black boots and a beauty spot. This was way outside my comfort zone. In those days, homosexuality wasn't openly discussed, and I'd never seen a transvestite. I wondered if all bars were like this. Fascinated, we decided to stay. Everyone was dancing by this point and the 40-year-old minibus driver with the moustache, who I now knew as Richard, asked me to dance to 'Ebony and Ivory' by Paul McCartney and Stevie Wonder. It was a bit of a slow one and Richard seemed quite keen. I was more worried about the age gap, but he did walk me back to the hotel. My roommate Jan said, 'Richard seems to like you.' I asked her how old he was. She wasn't sure, but thought 40 was a bit of an overestimate. I decided to steer clear of him the next morning. Perhaps, once the cider had worn off, he'd feel embarrassed. However, he came over to sit with me at breakfast, and we discovered we'd been paired up for mixed doubles. As the holiday progressed, he remained keen and, to my relief, confirmed that he was only six years older than me. The moustache had thrown me. Even so, he was 22, had a job and a car, and I was sitting my Highers exams!

When I was introduced to Richard's mum, dad and sister Louisa back in Scotland, they asked what school I went to. They were less interested in whether I attended a prestigious academic establishment – more that it wasn't St Something or other. Kirkintilloch High School received the desired response. After that, Louisa disappeared upstairs. She reappeared later on, stood right in front of me and asked, 'Where's Rhona?' How awkward! I considered a discreet wave, but no one else seemed to think this was odd. I thought Richard would've told me if his sister was visually impaired. But then all became clear. An old spaniel waddled into the room. My namesake had a growth under her tummy and her fur was falling out. I thought Richard might've told me he had a dog called Rhona! He never did understand the impact of failing to mention it.

That fateful trip to Belgium when I met Richard came a few months before I started medical school at Glasgow

University. I attended a full-time, full-on course for five years, but felt slightly dislocated from it in terms of the full student experience. I didn't share a flat, develop independent living skills, struggle to pay for food from my student grant or get involved in the whole student social scene. Instead, I lived at home and embarked on a serious relationship with my ginger-haired badminton partner. We saw each other every day, playing badminton five or six times a week. That meant I didn't have much time for studying. However, adjusting to self-disciplined study versus the spoon-feeding of my school days was a daunting process. And morphing from being a big fish in a small pond to becoming a small fish in the university ocean was even harder. Gone were the familiar faces of school friends, replaced by a lecture hall of 200 competitive, academically able strangers from all over the world.

CHAPTER 3

Making Friends with Albert

At first, I felt unhappy at university, a fish out of water. I wondered what I'd got myself into. My lab partners, William and Nigel, had both been to all-male private schools and stared at me in the lab as if I was an odd specimen. I assumed they were looking down their noses at me because of my comprehensive school education and Glaswegian accent but, with hindsight, I think it was simply because I was a girl. As time went by, they'd become good friends, but some adjustment was required. I'd come straight from the fifth year at school and had only studied two sciences (chemistry and physics), which was all that our curriculum timetable would allow. Some people had an A-grade A-level in biology, and I hadn't even done an O-level. It was a steep learning curve, especially when we were told, 'We'll get you all up to the same level of knowledge in the first six weeks.' This included mastering DNA, genetics and dissecting a still-warm rat, killed especially for me. I felt overwhelmed at the beginning. Being keen to learn, I tried to write down every scrap of information covered during the lectures, but when I attempted to write something like 'pseudo-stratified columnar ciliated epithelium' during the anatomy lecture, I wasn't sure I was going to survive the course.

Eventually, I settled in. Our labs and tutorials tended to be alphabetical, so most of my friends had surnames in the same part of the alphabet. The curriculum was intense, with full days of lectures, laboratories, clinical training sessions in hospital, and then the dreaded exam study. William and his flatmate David shared my pain, spending most lunch breaks and any free time between lectures chatting, drinking hot chocolate and eating warm Danish pastries in the little café in Ashton Lane. Well, William and I chatted like budgies and David often read the newspaper! Our friend Anna, a farmer's daughter from Lancashire, announced early on that she had a long-term aspiration to marry a Scottish man in a kilt. (Fast forward six years or so and a phone call from Anna revealed that she had fulfilled her dream: she was marrying Angus, who used to live in Kirkintilloch. I told her there used to be a boy in my reading group at primary school called Angus. Wouldn't it be funny if it was the same Angus? It was. I'd known him longer than her. What were the odds?)

During our diabetes module, we had to check our urinalysis and blood sugar. William appeared with the analysis stick dripping with fresh urine, looking distressed. It was showing sugar. Distress turned to anguish when I attempted to stab him on the thumb for a blood sample. It required a quick jab with a very sharp lancet, but I couldn't stab my best friend. Tentatively, I slowly pushed the lancet into the flesh of his thumb instead. I thought I was being kind! It was excruciatingly painful, bore no fruit and would require several attempts before we extracted the desired droplet. In the pain lab, we had to give each other increasingly powerful electric shocks to test our pain threshold. Nigel was determined to prove that he had the highest threshold, insisting that we turn the dial to maximum. This resulted in facial twitching. I worried that he might have a seizure! Oh, and William and David nearly poisoned me. Rather than washing their mugs, they just kept reusing them. Fortunately, I spotted furry green mould growing in the one that was about to host my teabag and chose a can of juice instead. It was sometimes a dangerous business being a medical student.

We also shared a dead body in anatomy, christening him Albert. I planted a tree in my garden in his honour. It was a huge sacrifice for the patient and his family to donate his body to science. We had Albert, preserved in formaldehyde, for the duration of our two-year anatomy course. It's hard to describe the pervasive stench and sight of about 40 dead bodies, all laid out on metal trolleys. We dissected Albert's heart on Valentine's Day and, when it was time to study the brain, it arrived in a bucket. The anatomy museum, which was en route to the anatomy lab, housed a collection of odd specimens in glass jars, including a cyclops baby and various other genetic abnormalities. Anatomy wasn't my forte; I had to do a resit. It was like learning a telephone directory, so I was (reluctantly) forced to retreat to Glasgow University's reading room on a regular basis. When I eventually got hold of my first psychiatric textbook, I was so keen that I immediately headed for the index to look up nervous breakdown. It wasn't there! I wondered what kind of textbook this was. I later discovered that nervous breakdown is a generic term used by the general public to describe some sort of non-specific emotional distress. It doesn't exist as a diagnosis – a bit like tummy ache, which isn't to be found in the textbook index for medicine or surgery. There was a lot to learn.

One night, at the end of second year, Richard arrived to rescue me from my studying, about an hour earlier than arranged. Although I hated studying, I was angry. I was on a mission to cover a set amount of telephone directory every night, to get it done in time for my second-year anatomy resit exam.

'I've been this way already tonight.'

I took the bait.

'Why?'

'I've been to see your dad.'

'What for?'

'I asked him if it would be OK if we got engaged.'

He'd never mentioned getting engaged. Was this a proposal of marriage? I think it was. I didn't see that coming! We got engaged a few weeks later, after we'd picked out a delicate solitaire diamond ring in the Argyll Arcade. It would officially take place during a romantic meal at Campsie Glen Country House Hotel. I subsidised my student grant by working in the lounge bar for a few shifts per month. My friends on the staff made a guard of honour and there were red roses and champagne. It was lovely. Well done, Richard.

CHAPTER 4

I Hate Reading!

During our medical training, we were required to write a dissertation on a topic of our choice. I hated reading, computers and statistics, so this was going to be fun. When one of my peers told me they were going to review the literature on treatments for breast cancer, I said, 'Oh, that would be a good topic to research.' But I was thinking, 'What a nightmare, there'll be a million references to read and summarise. I can't possibly choose a topic with lots of references – it would kill me.' I didn't know what to do. While I was waiting for a meeting with my supervisor, I picked up a medical journal and scanned the contents. To my surprise, an article piqued my interest. I read all of it, including the graphs, results, interpretation and conclusions. I strongly disagreed with the conclusions, which surprised me. It seemed to be saying that the normal population experiences a rise in blood pressure with increasing age, and that those with a diagnosis of schizophrenia experience a rise too, but this was less marked. Those with Down's syndrome, a chromosomal abnormality that causes learning disability and typical physical characteristics, had blood pressure recordings lower than everyone else, even other patients with learning disabilities (non-Down's).

Having spent every week of my life in a learning disability hospital visiting Vivienne, I felt qualified to express a view. The researchers concluded that the differences in the mentally ill patients were linked to them being institutionalised and better protected from normal life stressors. I accepted that the environment might be a partial explanation for their blood pressure changes, but it didn't explain those with Down's syndrome having the lowest blood pressure of all. In my experience they were the patients who often had specific roles with a degree of responsibility, such as delivering post between wards. They certainly weren't the most restricted or removed from stressors.

A kernel of an idea was forming. Could I look into this further? If I carried out new research, that would mean hardly any references to read, as I would be creating the evidence base. I had enough contacts to access patients with Down's syndrome and non-Down's syndrome learning disability living in the same hospital environment. I'd need to find a similar group who were living in community settings and would presumably be exposed to more environmental stressors such as getting on and off buses, going to the shops, etc. If environmental factors were the main cause, there would be a difference between the groups. If there was something specific to Down's syndrome that prevented them from experiencing age-related rises in blood pressure, then there would be little difference in the two populations of patients with Down's syndrome. I had a plan.

After discussions with the Medical Research Council Blood Pressure Unit at Glasgow's Western Infirmary, I secured support from Professor Lever to formulate my ideas and plan my project. A stereotypical professor, he had half-moon spectacles perched on the top of his head and, if he needed to remember something, wrote it on a Post-it and stuck it to his forehead. Fortunately for me, he had researchers who were tasked with conducting literature reviews. As I'd hoped, there were only a handful of papers to read. To avoid observer bias in taking blood pressure (BP) recordings, I was trained to use a random zero sphygmomanometer. Essentially, if you've ever felt an inflated BP cuff around your arm and thought it was a bit painful, multiply that by two. Normally you'd inflate the cuff to occlude the artery and then listen for the Korotkoff sounds that are produced underneath the lower part of the cuff when you start to deflate it. These sounds are heard when the blood pressure is between systolic and diastolic pressure. Turbulence occurs as blood starts to pump through the semi-occluded artery, as it collapses and reopens with each heartbeat. When the sounds disappear, that gives you the diastolic reading. You then deflate the cuff to allow the mercury to fall to zero. Unfortunately, that means you could be biased when listening for the cut-off sound, especially if you're expecting low blood pressure. However, this sphygmomanometer worked differently. You had to inflate the cuff to pressures much higher than normal and then, after recording the systolic and diastolic BP, you deflated the cuff. On each occasion, the mercury didn't fall to zero. The mercury levels changed on every recording. To calculate the actual BP measurement, whatever it levelled out at had to be subtracted from the two recordings you'd previously noted. For example, if the original recording was 180/110, you then had to subtract the final level of the mercury, which might be 60 and would thus give you a BP of 120/50.

I carried out the data collection across two learning disability hospitals and in a variety of adult training centres in the community. Parents and guardians were asked to provide consent for their relatives to participate, and any patient who didn't want to take part was excluded. Surprisingly, despite the pain of the cuff, most agreed to participate in multiple recordings over several visits. On reflection, I'm not sure if it was ethical to thank them with a sweetie, but attempts to reduce their stress levels seemed necessary. I spent time with them beforehand, hearing about their art projects and social outings, so that I wasn't just the stranger with the painful machine. The White Coat Effect is well documented and can result in people having higher BP measurements. We also planned to do 24-hour BP monitoring on a small subset, to look for any variation or fluctuation in BP recordings throughout the day and overnight. There was limited evidence relating to BP in older patients with Down's syndrome, as life expectancy in this population was impacted by a higher-than-normal incidence of congenital heart disease, plus early-onset Alzheimer's. I was fortunate that surgical intervention for heart problems was more commonplace by that time. I had an age range in my group of 16 to 65. When reviewing the data I'd collected, it became clear that statistical analysis wouldn't be required, as the results were so startling. Patients with Down's syndrome all measured BP well below that expected for their age and sex, and their BP did not appear to increase with age in either of the environments.

Some ten years later, I revisited my research as a higher trainee and did a ten-year follow-up study on the same cohort of patients. That's quite unheard of for a junior doctor. The topic clearly wasn't linked to forensic psychiatry, which had become my specialty by then, but I was happier to progress my original research project rather than start a new one just for the sake of it. I roped in my friend Alice for phase two of the study and was able to demonstrate that, as predicted, their blood pressure did not increase over the ten years, with measurements 30-40 mmHg below expected recordings, which was clearly statistically significant. I was, however, reliant on Professor Lever to explain it all. We collaborated and wrote a paper, which was to be the only serious research I ever had published. He invited me to present my paper at the British Hypertension Society conference. We met for lunch, during which he introduced me to his cronies, i.e. every professor of medicine from across the UK. Technically, I was probably the world expert in low blood pressure in Down's syndrome because no one else had examined it, but I knew that if the audience asked any questions, I'd be in trouble. I teed up my professor to step in for the Q&A if necessary.

Standing in front of a full auditorium, I spotted all of my new professor pals, which wasn't great for settling my performance anxiety and imposter syndrome. I started with a disclaimer: 'I am a senior registrar in forensic psychiatry. I would probably feel more comfortable talking to a room full of mentally disordered offenders.' A shout came from the audience: 'Feel right at home! This lot are a shower of crooks anyway!' In the end, I delivered my talk and emerged unscathed.

I still wonder whether or not chromosome 21 is a protective factor against the development of hypertension, but I'm unsure if anyone ever followed this up. I also presented my research to the Scottish Royal College of Psychiatry. Professor Lever insisted on coming along. He sat bemused by all of the psychiatric presentations, which were outside his knowledge base, but asked lots of questions anyway, half-moon spectacles firmly wedged on the end of his nose. It was a good day out with his 'girls', which is how he introduced me and my colleague to the professors.

CHAPTER 5

A Baptism of Urine

Lennox Castle stood at the top of a hill, with a selection of wards and prefabricated huts spreading out beneath it, each housing a particular patient group. Every summer during my break from university, I was allocated a different group to work with. On my first day, I was sent to an adult, male, long-stay ward. I entered with trepidation and was confronted by at least 30 naked men sitting on the edge of their beds and a pile of clothes in the middle of the floor. My induction was simply 'Dress the men.' It was a baptism of fire. Clothing appeared to be communal, and the pile contained lots of shiny, patterned Crimplene jumpers in shades of blue and brown; trousers of varying lengths in similar colours, often with no functioning zip; and a variety of socks, not paired. Being 17 and never having seen a naked man in the flesh before, I opted to dress a 90-year-old man. I went through a further baptism, this time of urine, as I pulled on his socks. Bath time involved two baths in the same room and a queue of naked men. Mealtimes were tricky, too. Some patients in adult prams had seizures as I tried to feed them porridge. Making the tea involved tea bags, milk and sugar, all in the same large pot. In my own small way, I tried my best to deliver individualised care, but it was a challenge. Many of the staff were related, as the hospital was the main employer in the local area. You had to watch what you said to them. Jungle drums would beat as staff warned each other that the doctor was on their way. Sometimes it was just me and a drunk charge nurse on duty. They stayed in the office while I managed mealtime for 40 patients, with four or five of them lying in adult prams and needing to be fed.

Before I left Lennox Castle that summer, I asked if I could take the patients to the hospital disco because I wanted to see them having fun. I was told I could go if I bathed all the men. Yet again, the charge nurse stayed in the office. I emerged from the ward with three patients: one walking independently, one hooked on my arm, and one in a wheelchair. There was great excitement when we arrived at the hall, as everyone was up and dancing to the music. The two mobile patients joined in. I lifted the small teenage boy, who was no bigger than a young child, out of his wheelchair. With his legs wrapped round my waist and hands round my neck, we spun in time to the music. His cries of joy made it all worthwhile. We had juice and cake as a special treat, so it was back to the wheelchair for that. He couldn't communicate verbally but flapped his arms at me, gesturing that he wanted to dance again, so I lifted him up. Hands covered with drool and sticky cake crumbs grabbed onto my tunic, and I developed a ring of confidence – well, a ring of urine – around my waist, as he became incontinent mid-number. When I arrived back on the ward, my colleagues thought they'd got one over on the naïve student, but I wouldn't have missed it for the world. Quality of life is what it's all about.

During another summer, one of the student nurses suggested that two male student nurses and I should take a group of patients out for a walk in the grounds. We must have had about six patients with us in total, with me pushing the one in the wheelchair and having a further two grabbing on to my arms on either side. We arrived at a reservoir that's now ingrained in my mind. The two male students disappeared behind a bush and, shortly afterwards, I heard them dive into the water and go for a swim, leaving me to care for six patients. An immediate return was not part of their game plan. Fortunately, I managed to corral the patients beside me on the grass and we ate some treats. Then, one of the student nurses returned, dripping wet, and said he'd take one of the male patients for a walk. They disappeared behind a bush for far too long. I couldn't investigate because I was in charge of five vulnerable adults close to water. Then I heard a splash from behind the bush and saw the patient in the water, arms flailing. What should I do? I screamed at the other nurse to help. Fortunately, he did. The patient arrived back in the group, wet and coughing up water, accompanied by two sheepish student nurses. They decided they needed to take the dry clothes from the man in the wheelchair for the wet patient who'd nearly drowned, and the patient in the wheelchair was wrapped up in a blanket to keep warm. What kind of place was this? In my mind, I was on a greater mission. I was going to change the world for patients everywhere. I did report the incident, but had no assurance it would be acted upon. If only I'd had the authority and knowledge to act back then that I had later on. There were professional conduct, health and safety and adult support and protection issues at play. I knew I was unlikely to change the culture of an old-style institution, but tried to model a different way of being because I respected and valued the patients I had the pleasure of nursing. I vowed I'd try to change things in the future.

Back at university, I continued to have noteworthy experiences, but not all of them were great. Watching a post-mortem wasn't high on my list of 'must repeat' activities. The special moments included experiencing the joy (and relief) of safely delivering 12 babies to grateful parents, and holding a premature baby that was as delicate as a baby bird and barely filled the palm of my hand. Then there was the time we headed out in an ambulance to assess a bleeding, pregnant drug user in a deprived part of town. We had to get someone to mind the ambulance, or we might have come back out to find it sitting on bricks, minus a few tyres. On arrival we were presented with the evidence in a pale blue basin, pulled out from under the couch. There were cigarette ends floating in the bloody fluid. I nearly threw up in the basin. On another day a group of us were sent to visit the sexually transmitted disease clinic in genitourinary medicine. A track-suited skinhead in the waiting room jibed, 'That must have been some party you were at!' Embarrassed, we skulked in to see the doctor we'd be shadowing for the afternoon. We covered everything from paediatrics, geriatrics and accident and emergency to medicine, surgery, pathology, psychiatry, obstetrics, gynaecology, orthopaedics, cardiology, respiratory, diabetes and ophthalmology, learning obscure facts we'd probably never use or remember. Interestingly, we didn't learn first aid or how to certify a body. I was, however, allowed to practise stitching on a drunk man's face and we took blood from each other a few times but then, before we knew it, we'd be let loose on an unsuspecting public.

Attending rounds in the different specialty wards usually involved me trying to remain invisible in an attempt to avoid the dreaded questions in front of a patient: 'What is the differential diagnosis, what are the causes, what investigations should be done, what treatment options should be considered?' It was a time for the swots to showboat and the fair-haired badminton player to hope the ground would open up and swallow her. I'd have my moments to shine when we headed for the psychiatry module. We were almost ready to become doctors, but there was the small matter of the surgical finals to overcome. For the timed practical examination, we had to take a history from our patient, examine them and review their X-rays before presenting our findings to the examiners. Tension mounted as we anxiously anticipated what was lurking behind the curtains that were drawn around each bed. The nurse beckoned everyone in, except me, allocating each student to their assigned patient.

'Your patient is using the commode; you'll have to wait.'

The clock was ticking, and sweat was dripping off me, but my patient and his bowels were in no hurry. I was eventually allowed in, to be confronted by a jaundiced man, his distended abdomen and a pungent odour. I'd lost a third of my allotted time to his diarrhoea. My attempts to take his history failed at the first hurdle. He slurred and drooled but nothing intelligible was forthcoming. As he pointed at his toothless gums, it became clear that he'd misplaced a full set of dentures. Undeterred yet somewhat desperate, it was time for me to improvise. I needed to identify the colour of his bowel motions. I noticed that the curtains around the bed sported a stripy autumnal design and helpfully featured all shades of bowel motion, so I was able to establish that he had white, fatty, floating stools and foul-smelling steatorrhea, which can occur during liver failure. Phew. Perhaps I might scrape through after all...

I couldn't quite believe it at the time but, in 1985, I emerged from the protective chrysalis of university as Dr Pollock, MBChB. I think Richard deserved a degree too, as he'd endured the trials and tribulations of the journey with me. There was still so much to learn. I'd managed to secure my junior house officer posts at the Southern General Hospital in Glasgow and would be doing the medical part of my job with my best friends, William, David and Anna. It couldn't have worked out any better. We had fun working together. One time, William popped his head around a patient's curtains and asked 'What's for tea, darling?' as the old lady had assumed that these two junior doctors, both called Dr Pollock, were married. He was always up to some nonsense.

CHAPTER 6

Goodbye, Vivvie

Vivvie spent 23 years lying in one position. Then, one day, she developed a bowel obstruction and had to be admitted to Stobhill Hospital. We were initially told she had urinary retention and had started bleeding when they catheterised her. We were told she may have von Willebrand disease, which would explain the bleeding (the disease means blood doesn't clot properly). It had never been mentioned before, which was concerning, as it was a genetically inherited disorder. I may have been a rookie medical student, but it seemed odd that they could have confused a bowel obstruction for urinary retention in a doubly incontinent patient wearing nappies. After a series of frantic family phone calls, we arranged to meet the ambulance at the hospital. I was intensely aware of the need for Vivvie to have an advocate and avoid any medical decisions being made that were based on biased assumptions. I tried to explain that she had a good quality of life and always seemed happy, despite her many disabilities and sensory impairment. It has always seemed so much worse to me when someone who has previously functioned normally has a catastrophic head injury and experiences loss of function and a change in personality. Their loved ones have lost the person they knew, and the injured party will no longer be able to fulfil their potential.

The day after admission, the pressure points on Vivvie's heels and knees were already looking a bit red, and we had concerns about the possibility of bed sores developing. It may have been the starched sheets, but all I knew was that she'd never had bedsores before. Despite Lennox Castle having had some bad press, her skincare had been excellent. Then came the dreaded phone call. We were needed urgently at the hospital. They wouldn't let us in to see her, instead ushering us into a side room to await the doctor. I felt a heavy feeling in the pit of my stomach. I knew what was coming. I'll never forget our encounter with that awkward junior doctor.

'I'm really sorry, Vivienne died a short while ago.'

She had aspirated her own vomit, having choked because she couldn't sit up. My world crumbled. This couldn't be real. She was only 23. I felt a huge, empty void opening up inside me. She was such an important part of my life. Dad said a prayer as we stood by her bedside. Everything seemed to halt in time and space as I tried to process what had just happened. Those looking on might have thought she had no quality of life, and it was a 'blessing', but she never knew anything different and was happy and contented in her own way. I felt as if I had lost my soulmate, but couldn't verbalise it. I'd spent time with her every Sunday, but now she had gone. Her life had meaning because she had shaped the future of every person around her bed. Mum worked in the learning disability section at the Department of Health and Social Security benefits office; Dad volunteered as a Samaritan, helping poor souls in crisis; and Elaine had decided to do a degree in religious studies. She'd initially intended to study languages, but I think it was her way of trying to make sense of what had happened to Vivvie. And here I was, training to be a doctor, with the aim of becoming a consultant in learning disability psychiatry. Vivvie taught me an important life lesson about always valuing people and never judging them. This shaped the core values of the doctor I became and that's how she lives on in me.

At the funeral, I was touched by the presence of some of the patients who'd shared Vivvie's home at Lennox Castle for all those years. It meant a lot to me that they'd come to pay their respects. I refused to wear black, preferring to celebrate her short life rather than mourn her death. Her coffin looked so small. As they committed her body for cremation, the coffin disappeared downwards under a velvet cloth. I'm not religious, but the symbolism of going down into hell was truly distressing.

Other patients I met during my summer jobs at Lennox Castle shared similar difficulties with sensory impairment. The most memorable was a deaf-blind patient whom I nursed in the long-stay wards, where I first encountered the T&P round, which involved serving sweet, milky tea from the communal teapot, then sitting the patients on a row of commodes to pee. It was inhumane. I was becoming increasingly concerned about the care and realised that this wasn't normal for the NHS. My patient had previously been able to see and had learnt sign language. Unfortunately, their subsequent loss of vision meant they now couldn't see what anyone signed back, so they lived in an isolated, cut-off place. If you took the time to sit down and hold their hand, they would teach you the deaf alphabet. They'd create the signs using their hand plus one of yours, so they could sense the change of sign when you touched their hand to spell out the word. It was their window on the world. I took the time to learn, but found myself on the wrong side of the charge nurse, who would say 'Stop slacking; you're wasting time talking to patients.'

During one mealtime, the main course was put down in front of this patient. Having explored the textures on the plate with their hand, they ate the food. When the nursing staff took their plate away, they started screaming and banging the table. The charge nurse considered them to be too disruptive and therefore instructed that they should be removed from the dining room. They would not be getting dessert. I directed them away and sat down, tentatively using my newly acquired signing skills to ask what was wrong. 'More mince!' came the agitated, signed reply. I was furious. Ironically, attempts to argue their case with the charge nurse fell on deaf ears. It was another valuable lesson in the importance of person-centred care: value the person and listen to what matters to them. This was rich learning for the summer student and aspiring doctor. Working with patients at Lennox Castle, especially Vivvie, taught me not to make assumptions about people and to communicate at their level.

CHAPTER 7

Clinical Kebabs

There are so many medical dramas on TV nowadays that we've created a nation of armchair experts. Patients' expectations are driven by the fast-paced decisions in American ER departments, where junior doctors crack open chests, squeeze hearts back to life, amputate limbs and manage multiple trauma victims, all in the course of a regular shift. The reality of the Southern General was a little different. When I was on call for medicine and surgery as a junior doctor, I can assure you I wasn't cracking open chests. We were just out of university, with a lot of textbook knowledge but limited practical experience, and there was often considerable debate before we did anything. If Dr Pimplepopper had been on the TV then, I might have taken a whole different career path, as I loved squeezing and squirting abscesses. There's something satisfying about all that cheesy pus and gunk. Gross, I know. However, there were some situations that university and TV medical dramas couldn't prepare me for.

Unlike the big Glasgow teaching hospitals, which had specialist teams for everything, the Southern General was a district general hospital and you and the registrars were pretty much on your own. It wouldn't be allowed nowadays, due to health and safety, rest days and the working time directive, but you certainly had some hands-on experience working from Friday morning straight through to Monday night without a break. We'd be working on Tuesday, as usual. Sleep was always interrupted by cardiac arrest calls, usually at the other side of the hospital. In those days, we had to collect the portable ECG machine, then run across the car park and up three flights of stairs. On most occasions it was touch and go whether they'd have to resuscitate me as well. If the route involved a certain long, dark corridor near the doctors' mess, you also had to dodge the scuttling cockroach brigade. One night, at about 2 am, we were in the canteen eating macaroni cheese, having just come out of theatre. The surgical senior registrar had written 'Barney' in block letters on the back of my white coat. I was raging. He and his anaesthetist pal used to sing 'Barney, Barney Rubble', a song from the cartoon TV series *The Flintstones*, while I was in theatre. It took me some time to realise that my blonde spiky hair reminded them of Fred Flintstone's best pal.

'Beep, beep, beep, paediatric arrest A&E' came echoing from the cardiac arrest pager in my pocket. The canteen was at the other end of the hospital, and the prospect of running any distance with macaroni cheese slopping about in my stomach didn't appeal. I panicked when I registered that the call was for a paediatric arrest. We weren't on the paediatric arrest team, for obvious reasons: we didn't know what to do with babies who weren't breathing or whose hearts had stopped. I've never run so fast. We both headed for the emergency department, worried about what we might find. A thud of a fist on a baby's chest was definitely not what would be required, but it was all I had to offer. As we rounded the corner of the hospital corridor that led to the emergency department, we were met by other doctors, who were also running but looked as if they might know what to do. The switchboard had realised their error and paged the correct team. It was a blue one-year-old boy.

I had further contact with the paediatrician that Christmas. Luckily, I was off on Christmas Day. However, the custom was that all of the staff came in to do the ward round, with the on-call doctors dressed as an elf and a fairy. My male colleagues looked lovely in tutus and tights. Richard came with me when we went round the wards and wished the patients a merry Christmas. An elderly man in the urology ward wanted a kiss... and I obliged. He had prostate problems and often needed his urethra stretched. It was always arranged to take place at Christmas, as he liked the ward, the company and the turkey dinner. But nobody mentioned he had shingles. Two weeks later, I was sent down to the emergency department to see the paediatrician for confirmation of a chickenpox rash. For a junior doctor working long shifts, two weeks' enforced time off was quite a result. But I was soon back at work, coping with district general emergencies. The surgeons were all in theatre when I got an emergency call from the ward: 'Mr Smith's got a pneumothorax [collapsed lung]. He urgently needs a chest drain.' I'd never seen one put in, far less completed such a procedure myself. The message from the surgeon, relayed via a theatre nurse, was 'Get it done.' It was a step too far for me. Fortunately, one of the registrars lived in hospital accommodation. He wasn't on call but kindly came in to supervise me. I trusted him to know what he was doing. The post-procedure chest X-ray showed the pneumothorax had resolved and the chest drain was in situ, resting just above the diaphragm. If he'd breathed at the wrong time we might have ended up with a diaphragmatic kebab.

The urology ward often features in my list of vivid memories. As a medical student, I remember being ushered into a room to be confronted by a man sitting in a bath with his penile tumour floating in the bubbles. On the same day, they switched off the lights and shone a torch behind a man's enlarged scrotum to light up his hydrocele (a collection of fluid around the testicle). I think the surgeon would have benefited from some sort of patient dignity training. Later, as a junior doctor in the same ward, I was asked to insert a catheter into a man who had urinary retention (full bladder, unable to pee). I was in the middle of feeding a rubber tube into his penis (urethra) and blowing up a small balloon to anchor it in place when I realised that I hadn't been to the toilet for about 16 hours. I'd been so busy that it hadn't been a priority. I had to stop mid-procedure and run to the toilet. Looking back, having an in-dwelling catheter would've been a great help as a junior doctor. I wonder why no one has ever thought of it.

Some months later, during a night shift, I was called back to the ward and asked to insert a suprapubic catheter (through the abdomen rather than the urethra) in a man with prostate cancer and urinary retention. Again, I'd never seen the procedure being performed or done it myself. The theatre nurse relayed the pronouncement of the surgeon on call: 'Just do it; the nurse will keep you right.' I was confronted by a pack of tubes and sticky pads and what looked like a metal straw with a very sharp end. The idea was to launch this spiky metal straw right through the abdominal wall into the distended bladder, feed the tubing in and drain the urine. All I could see was skin... what was underneath? I had visions of kebabbing the bowel, piercing the aorta (if I pushed too far), and was genuinely terrified. I started to press the metal through the skin. I was extremely tentative. Then I was told to push a bit further. What if I burst something? I kept going. At last, something started to come through the tubing. A gush of urine would have been good at this point, but no, it was a trickle of blood. Had I hit the aorta? If I pushed further, would I suddenly release a fountain of blood? Urine finally began to trickle out and the nurse showed me how to connect the tubing to the bag and secure them in place. It later transpired that the patient also had a bladder tumour, which no one had thought to mention. I had to go through that before entering the bladder with the tube. As you can see, working as a junior doctor wasn't for the faint hearted. There was the internal dialogue telling you that you weren't good enough; an unwritten rule that it wasn't good form to call the consultant for advice out-of-hours; and the fear that you'd get a bad reference if you got something wrong. My learning was: when I'm a consultant, I'll always strive to be approachable and supportive of junior doctors.

CHAPTER 8

Mr Onion Man

Communicating with children was another skill I had to master. There wasn't much in the way of guidance, so I used my initiative. One lovely young woman with Down's syndrome attended with her carer. She needed to have blood tests done, but was scared of needles. This is how the conversation went:

'Do you like Coca-Cola?'

'Yes.'

'Would you like a can?'

'Yes please.'

'Do you think that if you drink it, and then we put this needle in your arm, Coca-Cola will come out? Shall we try, and see?'

'OK.'

To avoid any doubt, it didn't, but we got the blood sample. A further challenge presented itself with a young child who was scared of doctors. How was I going to gain her trust? What could I say?

'Hi, I'm Dr Pollock, but you can call me Rhona. What's your name? I hear you've not been well. Is it OK if I listen to your chest? I've brought someone to help me – can you guess who?'

'I don't know.'

'It's Mr Onion Man.'

She smiled. Bizarre, I know, but I'd dismantled my stethoscope to draw an onion man wearing hobnailed boots on the inside of the flat surface that lies on the skin so that I could distract children. I still have it.

'Shall we see what he can hear, and then you can have a shot?'

Improvising was a bit more rewarding than simply following protocols all the time. I was using my communication skills to engage with patients rather than just working like a robot following step-by-step instructions. There's room for both approaches, but I've always struggled to channel my inner robot. I was happier with a less constrained approach that used my skills and judgment. You can have all the knowledge, protocols, equipment and medication in the world to deliver consistent, safe care, but if you can't engage with the patient and gain their trust, it becomes meaningless. Mr Onion Man's mission was to listen through layers of skin, fat and muscle to identify the pathology underneath. (Later, as a forensic psychiatrist, I would have to go commando with no stethoscope. The job was the same, though, which was peeling back the layers to see what was going on inside.)

As junior doctors we were constantly faced with firsts, which would stick with us as significant learning opportunities. No one taught me how to confirm that someone was dead, but I was supposed to know. You'd think it would be easy (no heartbeat, no breathing), but I swear plenty of living patients don't appear to have chest movement but are breathing and still alive, even if you can't feel a pulse or hear heart sounds through a fatty chest wall.

'We think Mrs Jones is dead. Can you come and certify the body?'

I arrived to find Mrs Jones propped up against pillows in her hospital bed. She had cornflakes all over her face, milk dribbling from her mouth and a wet patch on the front of her flowery nightie. She was stone cold. The nurse had tried to force-feed cornflakes to a dead body. That one was easy.

The open plan Nightingale wards were great for nursing observation, but there was no privacy for patients. How could we disguise a patient's death? The covered trolley would emerge from the curtained cocoon and trundle off down the ward, poorly patients wondering if they'd be next. Disinfectant merged with the sour odour of diarrhoea as bowels were purged pre-theatre. Patients would try to listen in to the doctors' hushed conversations. I had a notebook, as a certain junior doctor was about to get a whole bunch of tasks to complete. I listened and learnt how to interact with patients, sometimes noting how not to do it. I was going to have to deal with difficult conversations, giving bad news and managing challenging behaviour. Along the way I also made a few observations about how not to treat junior doctors. Humiliating them in front of patients doesn't usually build confidence and self-esteem or encourage team-building. Over time, the large Nightingale wards would be replaced by small patient bays with two to four beds, with a few single rooms for the really sick patients. Ironically, this would not always be good for patient care. Observation is more difficult; patients can feel isolated, they may have difficulty with eating and drinking and be missed, and so on. The balance between modern hi-tech care and human-touch care is a fine one. As a junior doctor, I liked the fact that the charge nurse made me write a prescription for sherry for every patient at New Year. For some patients, it would sadly be their last.

We were taught a lot about diagnosing and managing illness, but nothing about how to deal with sick doctors. I met my first mentally ill patient before my psychiatric training had even started. At the time, I knew that something was wrong with this particular colleague, but didn't recognise what was actually happening. They asked if I could help with a drip, as their 21 attempts had failed. I had visions of a Tetley tea bag in the bed, with thousands of perforations. They became so stressed after making an error with medication that they failed to medicate the entire surgical unit with antibiotics and didn't have time to see the emergency patient who'd swallowed a dart for a bet. A perforated bowel was more likely than a bullseye. My colleague's behaviour gradually became more and more odd. I was having to mop up the errors. After the ward staff started asking me to cross-match blood because my colleague had failed to do it, I spoke to the registrar, then the senior registrar, then the consultant. They all said they'd have a word, but despite my attempts to escalate my concerns, nothing seemed to be happening. It was becoming increasingly worrying with every shift. My colleague was clearly not coping, and I felt unsupported. With hindsight, some of the more bizarre behaviours they started to exhibit after that were possibly signs of a more major mental illness. It came to a head one weekend when I emerged from theatre, having assisted at an emergency operation. I arrived back in the ward to be confronted by the nursing staff shouting 'Get that doctor out of here!' A patient had stopped breathing after being given too much morphine, twice. Patient sorted, it was time to move this up a gear. This was becoming dangerous. I went to the chair of the surgical division, which was daunting for a newly qualified doctor. My colleague was eventually removed from frontline work and referred for assessment, support and treatment.

Mental illness or stress can affect anyone, so it was our responsibility to recognise when there were warning signs and try to get help. Working long hours as a junior doctor was extremely stressful, with limited support, little free time and even less sleep. I'm talking about a time prior to the introduction of the European Working Time Directive and mandatory breaks, rest days and limited numbers of hours worked per week. I was fortunate to live at home and had my boyfriend and badminton to offer welcome distraction. Some years later, I became aware that the pressures of the house job had proved too much for a junior doctor from my year group at university. He had shot himself in the on-call room during a stressful night shift. What a tragic waste. Later in my career, I tried to make sure that I gave my colleagues the support and space they needed when they experienced fluctuations in their mental health. It's ironic but, as a result of the positive changes in training and working conditions, I think some of today's newly qualified consultants are often emotionally less resilient. During their training, they have much more time off and rest periods built into their rotas to ensure they're not working excessively long hours or working when over-tired, which is clearly a patient safety measure. However, despite having more time off, the training is the same length, so they effectively have less experience under their belts when they qualify, and this can affect confidence, resilience and stress levels. The pressures of today's NHS also mean less time to meet for a debrief with the team or colleagues over coffee or lunch. That was where a lot of learning and support used to take place.

I was lucky enough to have my pillar of support in Richard. On 28 June 1986, two weeks before the end of my medical house job at the Southern General, we were married at St Mary's Church, Kirkintilloch. The wedding party were dressed in kilts and there was a bagpiper at the door of the church. Back then, rather than being worried about how we looked and how much it cost, it was all about making a commitment to each other for life. As a junior doctor on horrendous shifts, there was no time to consider dress shopping, weekend cocktail sessions and generally doing the pre-wedding flap. I'd drawn a picture of my ballerina-length wedding dress and had it made. And yet our wedding day was perfect. My only regret is refusing to have the ceremony filmed. At the time, video cameras were huge, bulky, intrusive machines. With hindsight, it would've been nice to have captured the moment for me to relive years later. Richard wasn't comfortable making a speech, so I wrote a poem for him, which mentioned the 'Mount Vernon Moaner' marrying Rhona (he was known for his fondness for complaining). I didn't have long to wait for him to start complaining, because the top tier of our wedding cake, which he'd specially requested to be plain, arrived full of sultanas and raisins. I'm not sure who was covering the ground-floor medical unit at the Southern General that day, because all of the doctors were at the wedding reception. We honeymooned in Austria, spending a week touring picturesque towns and cities, waltzing in Vienna, eating Sachertorte in Kitzbühel and dancing around the filming locations from *The Sound of Music* in Salzburg, before a week of climbing mountains in Mayrhofen. Well, that's not strictly true. We took a chairlift up and walked back down, so there was no mountaineering involved.

Much to my relief, just after I got married, I started a training post in general psychiatry at Dykebar Hospital, Paisley. My game plan was still on track. Dr Pollock, the junior doctor, had morphed seamlessly into Dr Morrison, the trainee psychiatrist.

CHAPTER 9

Tell Me About Your Genitals

During my training at Dykebar, I rotated to a different specialty every six months. These included general adult psychiatry, learning disability, drugs and alcohol, rehabilitation, psychogeriatrics, child and adolescent psychiatry and general hospital liaison psychiatry, plus some psychotherapy and eating disorders experience. I soon started to notice recurring themes, but wasn't too sure how significant they were. It started when I was told that our new senior registrar was called Dallas. I pictured a Stetson. We were to meet in the outpatient department to do a joint assessment. There was no Stetson in sight, but he thrust his hand in my direction.

'The name's Dallas. Are you interested in doing sex therapy?'

A bit bold for a first meeting, I thought. It turned out that he was referring to a couple who required sex therapy, and we were going to be doing it together. That case was followed by a series of four male patients where sex was also on the agenda. The first young man was referred because of anxiety and depression. He was a snooker player who'd been charged with kerb-crawling and masturbating in his car while watching prostitutes. I don't think the sheriff would have appreciated him saying he was practising his cueing action. Next, a young man was referred because of depression, which on closer investigation was linked to him having Peyronie's disease (a non-cancerous condition resulting from fibrous scar tissue that develops on the penis and causes painful curved erections). His erect penis was squint, and he said this was causing relationship problems. I wasn't sure how I was supposed to help with that. I think I suggested a referral to the urology consultant.

A further case involved a middle-aged man who had kindly agreed to help by being a patient in my examination for membership to the Royal College of Psychiatrists. I was allocated time to carry out the psychiatric assessment and, following that, present his case, my formulation, the differential diagnosis and my treatment plan to the examiners. My patient was a reasonably good historian of his own life and symptoms but, in my opinion, had a schizophrenic illness. I always assumed that patients who volunteered to assist in exams were keen to help the doctors pass and would therefore share any key pieces of information. As the clock was ticking, I asked, 'Is there anything else you want to tell me before we finish?' He replied, 'I'm worried about the size of my penis.'

A bell rang, signalling that my time was up. I was ushered through to speak to the examiners, not having had time to establish if the patient's concern about his penis was a lifelong one or a delusion. I decided it must be significant or he wouldn't have mentioned it. After presenting the case formulation, I added, 'The patient also disclosed a concern that his penis is too small, but I had insufficient time to explore whether this was delusional or reality based.' There were puzzled looks all round, followed by a short delay while they flicked through the case file in front of them.

'He's never told anyone else.'

I was unsure why he'd told me about his penis. However, we did have a weekly forum with the psychotherapist where we could talk about any difficulties we'd had with the therapeutic relationship and interpreting or managing transference or countertransference. (Transference is when the patient redirects emotions that were originally felt in childhood to the therapist. Countertransference is essentially the reverse, relating to the therapist's emotional reaction to the patient.) We could also discuss our own psychotherapy cases. Everything was interpreted as having a meaning; for example, their relationship with their parents and sex, and how this was being played out in the therapeutic relationship. I decided never to peel and bite into a banana during that forum. There was always a risk that it would be interpreted as anger against males, sexual frustration or something equally bizarre. Anyway, I fed back my first four penis cases and said, 'Is there something about me that makes people want to tell me about their penis? I'm starting to think I have Tell Me About Your Genitals tattooed on my forehead.'

During the day, we had ready access to consultants for supervision and advice, but the unwritten rule during the night was to try not to disturb them. As the on-call doctors, we looked after several hundred inpatients at Dykebar and also had to cope with psychiatric emergencies sent over from A&E at the district general hospital. We did have an odd on-call rota, though. In addition to the junior doctor resident at the psychiatric hospital campus, there would be one at home who could be called in to deal with any issues in the two admission wards based at the district general site. If I was called in from home in the middle of the night, Richard would offer to chauffeur me to the hospital, driven by his belief that I'd probably fall asleep at the wheel. It meant more snooze time in the car, so there were no complaints from me. One winter's night, it was too cold for him to sit in the car for an hour, so he came up to the ward. The lights were dimmed, the patients were all tucked up in bed and the nurses were doing their rounds. He plonked himself at a small desk in the ward corridor, as he couldn't sit alone in the office that housed confidential patient records.

I headed off to see a distressed patient in their bedroom. Emerging about 45 minutes later, I found Richard chatting to someone at the desk. He looked relieved as he spotted me coming towards him and stood up, making his apologies to his companion. As he turned to face me, I could see a look of panic in his eyes. It turned out that, mid-conversation, the member of staff he'd been chatting to had started talking about his spaceship and his concerns about X-rays coming through the window. Richard had suddenly realised that this was not a member of staff; it was a psychotic patient. In fact, the patient posed no danger; he was just someone's son, brother, husband, dad who had developed a mental illness and was having difficulty sleeping. That night, Richard discovered that mental illness can happen to ordinary people who don't necessarily look, dress or act differently. However, mental illness is not always visible. So, check in with the people around you and remember to ask how they're doing. They may be feeling hopeless or tormented by hallucinations and delusions and need a helping hand to access support from specialist services. And a side note for any nurses out there: wear your name badge. There was a trend in mental health services for staff to wear their own clothes, with the aim of building trust and breaking down the 'them and us' barrier. Patients wandered around the ward freely, rather than being in bed in pyjamas, unless on observation due to specific concerns such as suicide risk. Those patients would have a nurse in tow. Visitors to the ward, as well as patients, might find it hard to identify the staff. If I arrived in an unfamiliar ward to do an assessment, I'd usually head for the ward office. I tended to avoid eye contact and address the wall, as sometimes the patients who had popped in for a chat looked more like staff than the staff did. Some patients got wise to the confusion and would approach visitors on arrival, pretending to be staff. I would always look for clues: furry slippers or a bandage over self-harm scars usually gave it away.

As I gained more experience, I got to know the staff, and the day job became a bit less stressful. However, this also meant being given more responsibility, so I was soon tasked with putting together the on-call rota. I'm unlikely to forget the Friday afternoon when I found out that no one wanted to work the weekend shift. Someone had called in sick and everyone was claiming to have commitments they couldn't get out of. Having worked the night shift the day before, I was understandably tired and preoccupied. While driving home at 5 pm, I suddenly found myself underneath a flatbed lorry, with the back of the lorry having smashed through my windscreen before my mangled car came to a halt. It had seemed as if time was moving really slowly, and I couldn't get my brain or feet to react. I watched like a bystander at an accident, never managing to hit the brakes. I heard the crunch of metal catching on metal as the underside of the lorry ripped back the front of my bonnet. I desperately tried to rewind in my head, trying to make sense of what had just happened. I remembered seeing the traffic lights ahead change to green, so I kept driving at 20 miles per hour in crawling traffic. It transpired that the lorry had been obscuring my view of a vehicle in the side street which the lorry had stopped to let into the queue of traffic. Worried onlookers came over to check that I was OK. I was clearly in shock. It had all happened in a few seconds. I automatically wiggled my neck and feet and decided that I wasn't injured. My driver's side door had also scrunched up like a concertina and was jammed shut, so I climbed over the passenger seat and out of the side door.

'Are you OK? You must have whiplash.'

'Don't worry – it's OK, I'm a doctor.'

What was I thinking? Did being a doctor make me immune to injury? The police arrived and took control of the situation. Teatime traffic was backing up on the road behind us. They asked the lorry driver to drive forward. My car was dragged forward with it, the metal of the bonnet mangled around the underside of the lorry. The friction of metal on metal caused it to spark. I started shrieking that the sparks would ignite the pool of fluid that had leaked onto the road, but the police reassured me and continued to try to separate the vehicles. Meanwhile, I made a garbled call to Richard.

'I've been in an accident. They're towing my car away. I've written it off. I was only doing 20 miles an hour.'

'Are you OK? Don't be ridiculous, calm down, you won't have written off your car.'

I had. The whole engine block had been pushed down and out of alignment. The policeman came over to take my statement. He didn't breathalyse me or charge me for careless driving. He just stood there, stroking my mohair jumper.

'I could stroke that all day,' he said. Carry on, officer.

Chapter 10

Are You Wearing a Sanitary Towel?

'Rhona, there's an emergency patient in outpatients for you. I don't know his name.'

How was I going to identify the emergency patient in a busy waiting area? An intoxicated young man in the corner shouted, 'Hello darling, are you here to see me?' I invited him into my office and he followed, accompanied by his girlfriend, who was also under the influence. It's easy to make assumptions. I could've thought 'Another drunk', but I attempted to carry out a psychiatric assessment. As a junior psychiatrist, I needed the practice.

'So, why have you been sent up to see me today?'

'What colour are your knickers?'

People often change their underwear before they go to see the doctor, but they don't normally ask about the doctor's underwear. I could've put this down to him being cheeky and disinhibited due to intoxication, but I logged it as unusual. He was now staring at an elastic band on my desk.

'Elastic band, hear the band, hear the band.'

He lifted the band to his ear to listen to it, which was clearly not normal. It was my second clue that something more than intoxication might be at play here. He was disinhibited in the content of his speech, with ideas that jumped around and were difficult to follow. His speech was also loud and pressured and he was rhyming and punning his words. Eventually, having established that he also had excess energy, insomnia and had been overspending, I concluded that an inpatient assessment was merited, as I thought he may be suffering from hypomania, which is essentially the opposite of depression.

'Can you please wait in the waiting room with your girlfriend while I contact the ward to book you a bed?'

While on the phone, I heard a commotion in the waiting area and went out to investigate. Most of the patients who'd been waiting when I arrived had disappeared into different interview rooms to see their own psychiatrist or psychologist. A middle-aged, rather haggard-looking woman remained in the corner. I guessed agitated depression, as she looked anxious, fidgeting nervously in her seat and wringing her hands. My patient was singing. He turned towards the anxious lady and bellowed, 'Are you wearing a sanitary towel?' I didn't wait for the nurses to arrive to escort him to the ward. I extracted him and deposited him in the ward before he caused any more trouble. I often tell this story to students. It's quite funny, but maybe not so funny if the drunk man had been a bank manager acting out in front of customers, or a clean-living priest blurting it out during a religious ceremony – or even your dad. Hypomanic patients often act out of character and can be sexually disinhibited, be promiscuous or strip off. The stigma and consequences could be significant, impacting their relationships or employment and could even result in criminal charges. It serves as a reminder of why it's important for people to respect and manage their illness and demonstrates why we sometimes use the Mental Health Act in such cases. It protects disinhibited and insightless patients from acting on grandiose delusions and being sexually disinhibited. Occasionally people present as much more overtly unwell. Such as a man wearing a cowboy hat and Hawaiian shirt (in winter) who spontaneously attempted to do a headstand against the door in my office, had bought 12 magnums of champagne and wanted to take me to Australia. I declined.

Patients' attire or behaviour would often provide clues to some abnormality of mental state. The out-of-hours interview room was along a corridor adjoining the two admission wards. One night, the wards were busy and there were no nurses available to do a joint assessment, so I'd be seeing a new referral on my own. The bushy-bearded gentleman removed his parka, with its orange lining and big furry trim around the hood, to reveal a bare chest and tie. A pair of bright, patterned underpants, worn over his trousers, completed the ensemble. I wasn't expecting Superman! The assessment proved to be awkward, as it was difficult to keep him on track and he was clearly delusional.

'I want to see inside that cabinet. Are you recording this?'

He pulled open the drawer of the filing cabinet to check and, finding it empty, sat down. I continued the assessment.

'They'll never know we've done it before,' he said, staring at me intensely.

Alarm bells started ringing in my head. Am I about to become that junior doctor who was raped during the night when she was doing an emergency assessment on her own? I attempted to distract him.

'I sense you're feeling quite uncomfortable with all of these questions. Perhaps you'll feel less anxious if I ask a nurse to join us?' (Subtext: at least I will!)

Before he had a chance to answer, I was out of the room like a shot. After that incident, the advice about carrying panic alarms, seeing new patients with two staff in the room and sitting nearest the door all made sense. As junior psychiatrists working overnight on a district psychiatric hospital site, we were totally on our own. We had several hundred patients to care for, both in terms of their mental and physical health. I had to cope with a pneumothorax and a case of acute stridor, except I couldn't remember the term stridor, so I improvised by making a rasping noise down the phone to the medical registrar at the general hospital (stridor is a noisy, high-pitched sound made when there is an upper airway blockage). It wasn't my finest hour. My major challenge was trying to resuscitate a lady who'd keeled over in the waiting room. She'd come for psychiatric assessment and had gone into cardiac arrest just as I arrived to call her into my office. There was no cardiac arrest team on a psychiatric hospital site, just me. Unfortunately, she didn't survive. But our group of trainee psychiatrists were very supportive of each other, and we survived the lonely on-call shifts by camping out by the hospital switchboard with the friendly operators, sometimes sharing a carry-out meal and hospital gossip. More than 30 years later, a group of us still meet up. Intense shared experiences tend to create long-lasting bonds.

During my child psychiatry rotation, I started to wonder why I'd spent five years at medical school, a year as a junior house officer and then several years in adult psychiatry. My first case was a four-year-old boy who was refusing to poo in the toilet. He was constipated and refused to eat. Here I was, after all that training, just a trainee poo detective. We'd been told that children relax and talk more if you play with them, so I was on my hands and knees at the sandpit, absolutely clueless about what I was doing, and not even that accomplished at building sandcastles. I established that his cat had become faecally incontinent, with blood in its faeces, and had left piles of bloody poo behind the settee (not quite his words, of course). Eventually, his furry friend was diagnosed with a tumour at the base of its tail and had to be put down. My new sandpit buddy had developed an anal fissure due to constipation and straining, which led to blood in his poo too.

'Your pussycat had blood in its poo.'

'Uh-huh.'

'You had blood in your poo too.'

'I don't want to go to the vet!'

My four-year-old patient thought he was going to be taken to the vet to be put down because he had bloody poo, just like his pussycat. Case solved. Turns out I wasn't that bad a poo detective after all.

CHAPTER 11

Finding Forensic

Between all the shift work and playing badminton with Richard five nights a week, I found it hard to fit in studying for the Royal College of Psychiatrists' membership examinations. I should probably have cut back on the badminton but, as you now know, I hated studying. However, we were unable to apply for a senior registrar training post in the sub-specialty of our choice until we had passed parts one and two of the exam. I'm not particularly proud to reveal that I had three attempts at part one. However, I sat part two in the same year that I passed part one. My tutor didn't even ask about the result of part two, assuming I would probably have failed. Much to his surprise, I sailed through part two at the first attempt because I'd read the textbooks for part one so many times.

I soon started scanning the *British Medical Journal* for job adverts, hoping to secure one of the two national training posts in learning disability, which was the reason I'd trained as a doctor and then as a psychiatrist. To my dismay, they were both taken and wouldn't be vacated any time soon. That scuppered my long-term career plan. However, there was an ad for the senior registrar position in forensic psychiatry, so my tutor suggested that I spend a week with a consultant from the high-secure State Hospital at Carstairs to find out more about it. I will be forever grateful for that opportunity. I'm interested in people, and the people I met were very interesting. It was a privilege to meet the faces behind the headlines and hear both sides of the story. In those days, forensic psychiatry wasn't one of the sub-specialties that junior psychiatrists were able to rotate to, so while I'd heard of it, I had no idea what it was. When I thought of 'forensic', I thought of crime scenes. Having had no knowledge or experience of forensic psychiatry at that point, I envisioned a prison-like environment, white coats and straitjackets. The reality was that, behind the high-secure perimeter fence, there were no white coats nor mechanical restraints in sight. Instead, I found wards that weren't that dissimilar to those in my own hospital, an aviary, bowling green, lots of green space and workshops where people were making rocking chairs. After a week of meeting mentally disordered offenders in the secure hospital, murderers on remand in prison whom I'd seen featured in the *Daily Record*, and visiting a number of prison psychiatric clinics, I was hooked.

I applied and was accepted for the three-year training post based at the Douglas Inch Centre in Glasgow, a forensic psychiatry community outpatient service that was unique in the UK at that time. Most forensic psychiatrists across the UK worked in medium- and high-secure units. That has always struck me as odd, as the skills in risk assessment and management which are specific to forensic psychiatry are mostly used in theoretical terms in these settings due to the physical, procedural and relational security in place. As a result, opportunities for testing out risk are limited, but that's not the case in a community setting. Most of the risk management measures in hospital settings are limited within the community and risk therefore fluctuates day to day, due to lack of physical security and potential access to weapons, victims and illicit substances. There's also the added risk of non-compliance with medication and disengagement from services. Working in a community setting definitely appealed to me more as it presented a personal challenge. Engaging with patients and developing a therapeutic relationship would be key. Most people spent three years as a specialist registrar before applying for a consultant post. I had the luxury of doing the job for six years as I didn't fancy any of the posts that did come up and, in those days, there was less pressure to vacate training posts. Trainees now have three year-long placements, and therefore their experience is somewhat limited, dictated to some degree by the interests of the trainer, where they work and how good they are.

I was fortunate to be able to organise my own training scheme. I moved jobs every six months for six years. I chose a topic and developed clinical training opportunities around it. For example, when working with adolescent offenders, I worked for one day a week in the young offenders' institution (males under 21); one day a week running a cognitive and behavioural skills group for school refusers and truanters (on the verge of institutional care); wrote all of the court reports for young offenders in my outpatient clinic; and ran a clinic and carried out staff training in the secure school. The topics covered included female offenders, male offenders, learning disabled offenders, substance misuse, sexual abuse, the Mental Health Act (Mental Welfare Commission), medium-secure care (Manchester/Northampton) and high-secure care (State Hospital). Throughout, I also spent one day a week working in intensive care general psychiatry in a variety of local hospitals.

It was at the start of my senior registrar training in forensic psychiatry that I had my second encounter with a sick doctor. The case involved a patient who could've done with some underwear. She had a paranoid schizophrenic illness with religious delusions and had been standing in the crucifix position outdoors, in zero degrees, with no socks or shoes on. I saw her in the surgical ward where she'd been treated for frostbite, having nearly lost both of her feet. In order to ensure compulsory injectable medication and engagement with services, I detained her under the Mental Health Act. Her recent illness relapse had occurred in the context of disengagement from services and non-compliance with medication, which was unfortunately an all-too-common sequence of events. Patients often believe they are well and don't need to take any more medication. In those days, in order to make the case for the detention order, we had to attend the sheriff court. It was one of the first times I had to give evidence in court as a higher trainee.

It should have been a slam dunk. I would have to get used to dealing with the courts, but no one said anything about needing legal representation. The mental health officer social worker (MHO) was doing his first detention. He'd spoken to the council solicitor, who thought it was a straightforward case. To our surprise, the patient turned up with a lawyer and a second opinion psychiatrist, which was her right. They'd sneaked in to assess her the night before. I hadn't been back to the ward, so I was unaware. Bizarrely, the psychiatrist who'd been instructed by the patient's lawyer stood up to give evidence and announced, 'The patient has an anxiety disorder that can be treated at home by social workers.' I was confused and thought this was nonsense. I asked the MHO if I could go back up to give further evidence, and the sheriff agreed. I stated, 'In no psychiatric textbook that I've ever read has it said that paranoid or religious delusions can be explained by anxiety and treated by a social worker in the community without antipsychotic medication.' By this point, I was seriously concerned that I might never get a reference or work again. However, it turned out to be a pivotal moment in my career. Telling the truth, based on my professional judgement, was going to be crucial, even if I disagreed with another expert. I had to start believing in myself. The MHO later admitted that he had no idea how to challenge in court, so had relied on the knowledge he'd gained from watching the TV programme LA Law. I discovered later that the doctor who provided the second opinion might actually have been unwell too, and that could've affected their judgement. I survived to see another courtroom.

CHAPTER 12

Don't Dismember Me

I was gradually maturing into the type of psychiatrist I aspired to be. I was never destined to be an academic or the fount of all knowledge, but I had confidence in my communication skills, which was crucial for engaging patients. Another of my Vivvie learnings was how important it was to engage with people at a level they could understand. In my opinion, people who use big words either have no insight into the average reading age of adults, or are trying to be superior. I recall a case involving a deaf patient with learning difficulties who was on an indecent exposure charge. I had booked a British Sign Language (BSL) interpreter for the assessment. The charge was described as 'lewd and libidinous behaviour, involving exposing a private member'. It brings a whole new meaning to a private member's bill. Interviewing with an interpreter present was new territory for me. I was supposed to be interpreting the patient's eye contact, body language and responses to the questions as they were being relayed to me via the interpreter. Instead, I was distracted by the gestures in my peripheral vision.

When patients have a learning difficulty, it's best to use short, open questions using simple vocabulary to ensure they understand what you're asking and reduce the risk of them saying what they think you want to hear. I had to deal with the combination of a patient with learning disability and deafness and a BSL interpreter who was signing, so taking a sexual history was proving to be a challenge. I pointed at the patient's genitals: 'What do you call that?' He might not know the term penis. I needed to discuss whether he touched it or played with it and what got him aroused. He just smiled and giggled. I asked again, needing a response. I was distracted by the simulated masturbation of the interpreter to my right. This assessment did not go well. Working with offenders who had communication challenges definitely made the job more difficult.

Having said that, some offenders were surprisingly easy to communicate with. HMP Barlinnie, Glasgow's notorious adult male prison, had quite a reputation, but the Special Unit was in a different league. It was famous for one of its inmates, Jimmy Boyle, a former Scottish gangster and convicted murderer who went on to become a sculptor and author. His autobiography, A Sense of Freedom, was later turned into a film. From my reading, I understand that he always denied the killing, but did admit to being a ruthless and violent enforcer from the Gorbals, which was a rough and deprived area of Glasgow. He also hit the news when he married Dr Sara Trevelyan while still a prisoner. She was an English doctor who was working in Scotland as a psychiatrist. They'd met in his prison cell after she contacted him having read his book. It was not a work-related encounter. I was sent to the Special Unit on one of my six-month special interest placements as a forensic trainee. It was a small, stand-alone unit in the grounds of HMP Barlinnie, which was lovingly referred to as the Big Hoose or the Bar-L. The Special Unit, which was functional between 1973 and 1994, was tasked with the rehabilitation of some of the most violent and volatile prisoners within the Scottish prison estate. The tabloid press described conditions within the unit as being like a holiday home, and indeed it was very different from other prison settings. Superficially it may have looked as if dangerous prisoners were being rewarded for bad behaviour, but it was actually an attempt to break the cycle of violence and rioting. They were serving such long sentences already that further sentences for additional violence in custody were not a deterrent. There was no incentive to behave. Rather than being treated like animals, long-term prisoners were given some autonomy and responsibility. They were required to behave in a prosocial manner in order to retain their privileges, learn new skills and remain in the unit. They wanted to stay, and therefore began to police themselves and behave in a more appropriate manner.

In terms of attitude and behaviour, staff selection was crucial, as they'd be required to interact in a very different way. I found myself on the interview panel. It felt more like a therapeutic community, with meetings and decisions made by consensus. This may sound easy, but for impulsive, antisocial, potentially violent men with huge egos and reputations to maintain, this would require considerable restraint. It was classic behaviour management: reward good behaviour and it's more likely to be repeated. Asking them to show respect, negotiate and resolve conflict without resorting to antisocial, violent behaviour was the most difficult thing we could've asked them to do. If a violent offender was being released and moving into the house next door to me, I'd have preferred him to have experienced that environment and learnt some alternative anger management strategies.

Rather than being locked up in seclusion and being fed through the hatch in the door by an officer in riot gear (yes, I visited a prison wing elsewhere where that was still happening), they had plenty of privileges and were allowed to decorate their cells. They would decide if they wanted to have a word with you or not. After the community meeting, 'TC' Campbell, famous for the drug-related ice-cream wars case in Glasgow, asked me, 'Do you want a chat?' This seemed innocent and safe enough. What could possibly happen? It was a prison. There were officers, right? But, as I followed him from the group room past the kitchen with its large selection of carving knives on the wall, it became clear that the cell area was a largely officer-free zone. I was there for two-and-a-half hours, and nobody came to check on me. I could've been raped, murdered and dismembered with a huge carving knife and no one would have known. As I said, the unit ran on trust, so these violent men effectively policed themselves. It was an interesting concept, although I think the previous management had given too many concessions and so, by this point, it felt a bit out of control. You may have guessed from the fact that I went on to have a career as a consultant forensic psychiatrist that I didn't get raped, murdered or dismembered, but catastrophic fantasising is inevitable when you're in a situation like that.

I was interested to note the decor of TC Campbell's cell. It had normal dimensions, with bars on the window, but he had wooden shutters over the bars to make it more homely. There was a fireplace with small red lamps and fake logs along one side and a bed settee on the other, with a shelf of legal books on the wall. He explained his legal position in great detail, along with why he was innocent, having clearly gleaned a lot of knowledge while researching and arguing the legal merits of his defence. I declined his offer of a cup of tea, with my paranoia and negative thinking now on overdrive. Will I get out alive? Will the tea be drugged? Where are the officers? There are knives out there – am I safe? How judgemental of me. My host was polite and non-threatening, but I was young, naïve and making assumptions. It was yet another valuable learning experience. Since then, I've prided myself on assessing people as I find them and not completely biasing my view with a tabloid story. It made me more aware of the actual danger, rather than allowing my judgement to be obscured by overactive internal dialogue. I considered risk assessment and management to be the most important aspects of the job. I never forgot the crimes that were committed, but my role was to take account of past risk behaviour, assess current risk and treat and manage illness, not to judge or punish.

TC Campbell and Joe Steele spent nearly 20 years in prison for the murder of six people. In 1984, they were accused of firebombing the Doyle family's tenement flat in Glasgow, which only the mother, Lilian, survived. The murders were alleged to have been linked to the Glasgow ice-cream wars, in which rival drug gangs tried to take over ice-cream van routes. The vans drove around housing schemes as a front for selling drugs and stolen goods. The Doyle family refused to give up their Garthamlock ice-cream route to the drug gangs, and thus became targets. During their lengthy period of incarceration, Campbell and Steele continued to protest their innocence until they were eventually cleared and released following a successful appeal in 2004. You may be familiar with the 1984 film, *Comfort and Joy*, a Scottish comedy written and directed by Bill Forsyth. It stars Bill Paterson as radio DJ Allan 'Dicky' Bird, whose life undergoes a bizarre upheaval after his girlfriend leaves him. He witnesses a baseball bat attack on an ice-cream van by angry competitors and becomes involved in the struggle between two Italian families over the ice-cream market in Glasgow. In an attempt to negotiate a peaceful settlement, the suggested solution is ice-cream fritters. This may sound odd, but Scotland's fish and chip shops are known for having invented deep-fried Mars Bars, so anything is possible. What does this have to do with TC Campbell and my role as a forensic psychiatrist? It isn't too much of a leap to suggest that the idea of turf wars between ice-cream van owners may have been influenced by Glasgow's real-life, drug-related ice-cream wars. The more bizarre link is that I was an extra during the filming of *Comfort and Joy*. I recall being paid £21 and being given some lunch in return for dressing up in winter clothes and wandering around Fraser's department store in Glasgow while the actors were filming a scene. Guess who got cut from the film after all that top-class acting?

Chapter 13

Picking Potatoes for Mother

The Special Unit was unlike other prison environments. Elsewhere, in other prisons, we had to interview prisoners wherever we could find a space. There wasn't always a nice interview room vacant in the prison health centre, although that was my favourite. On one occasion I found myself being ushered into a records cupboard. Surrounded by walls of files, I was virtually rubbing knees with an intimidating young man as he told me about his links to the IRA and whom he planned to murder (I would have to inform him that I'd need to report this risk to a named victim). It was literally too close for comfort. Some fancy verbal footwork would be required. The same scenario was repeated in the rooms for visiting professionals, where fixed furniture led to close proximity to prisoners for whom dental hygiene didn't appear to be a priority. Trying to carry out a 90-minute interview without breathing through your nose is quite the logistical challenge. If they hadn't washed for a while either and were wearing Eau de Damp Dog, it could actually be quite nauseating.

During my training, I also went to HMP Inverness for the Committee for Difficult Prisoners visit, which was a further attempt to control antisocial behaviour. We met a prisoner who was considered to be a high absconding risk and was housed in what were nicknamed 'the cages'. It was the nearest that I've come to a *Silence of the Lambs* scenario, with a cell that had floor-to-ceiling bars as well as a second row of bars. All that was missing was the 'fava beans and Chianti' conversation. Again, the story, the fantasy and the reality were quite different. Of course, the prisoners have often been found guilty of extremely violent behaviour and custodial care is merited for public protection, but if all that you can see is a dangerous man, you'll be inhibited in your understanding of what life experience or illness may have contributed to him becoming a dangerous man, and how these experiences have impacted his personality development and subsequent behaviour. Any attempt to reduce future risk will require this level of understanding.

Visits up north to attend this committee with the consultants were often entertaining. I was picked up at my house by my new boss, and only 20 minutes into the three-hour journey, panic set in. Feeling unusually warm down below, I thought, 'Surely not, I can't have wet myself in the consultant's car?!' I was so preoccupied I could barely manage stilted conversation. I wondered how I was going to explain this one. Then he said, 'Are you warm enough? Do you want me to turn off the heated seat?' We arrived in Inverness and headed for the guest house, which had been pre-booked by administrative staff at the State Hospital. The receptionist welcomed the consultant like an old friend but then looked a bit awkward, realising that I was with him.

'I'm really sorry, but I've only got one room in the booking and we're full.'

'I'll sleep in the car,' bellowed the consultant.

'No, I'll be fine,' I replied. 'I'll get a B&B nearby and meet you in the morning for breakfast.'

Telephone booking made, we set off, me and my six-foot, bearded luggage handler. But we didn't realise that there was a Ness Road, Ness Drive, Ness whatever, and hadn't really paid attention to the address. As we approached number five, it didn't look like a B&B. There's usually a small telephone table by the door, with leaflets about fun things to do in the local area, plus a lamp and a plant. This one had an overweight, half-dressed man.

'I'm not a B&B,' he said.

We'd already guessed that from the pale flesh and hair protruding through his string vest. Two further attempts at Ness-something-or-other and we felt confident that this one had all the hallmarks of a B&B. I looked expectantly at the owner.

'I have a booking.'

He looked at me and my towering escort, who must've been at least twice my age.

'I'm really sorry, we only have one single room left, not a double.'

In unison: 'We're not together.'

Him: 'I'm just carrying her bag.'

We agreed to meet for breakfast at his hotel. Representatives from the Scottish government would be staying there too, as they also attended the Committee for Difficult Prisoners. Having recovered from the previous night's uncomfortable encounter, I was starting to find the whole scenario rather amusing. I recounted the tale to a man from the government, my consultant almost disappearing under the table with embarrassment. On the return journey, after the meeting and prisoner reviews, he announced, 'Do you mind if we stop at my holiday home to pick potatoes for Mother?' So, off we headed, up a dirt track towards a collection of new-built bungalows on the hillside. After giving me a tour, he went off to pick the potatoes. Hurtling back down the dirt track towards the main road, he spotted his holiday home neighbour driving towards us. Waving him down, he screeched to a halt, keen to introduce me in an exaggerated voice: 'This is my *colleague*, Dr Morrison.' I think he was panicked by the fact that his neighbour had seen him up at the holiday home, on his own, with a young blonde.

On a subsequent trip to Peterhead and Inverness with a different consultant, I had yet another awkward experience. The Committee for Difficult Prisoners jaunt should have been renamed the Trip for Difficult Situations. This one had a bit of a reputation as a lady's man, so I was on guard. We stopped outside Aberdeen for tea, but it turned out to be a candlelit dinner. I felt uneasy. Thankfully there were two rooms at our hotel, just across the corridor from each other. We arranged a time for breakfast and said goodnight. As I emptied my overnight bag there was a knock at the door. I tentatively opened it.

'Come over and see this,' he said.

What could I do? I crossed the hallway and peered into his room.

'What do you make of that?'

There was a large four-poster bed. Oh my god, what was I supposed to do now?

'You're lucky. I got twin beds. Goodnight!'

I beat a speedy retreat. After making sure the door was locked, I went to bed. I'll never know if there was anything calculated about his behaviour, but it made me feel very uncomfortable. I recall a similar situation in HMP Barlinnie health centre when a male member of staff refused to move when I was trying to collect case notes. I had to squeeze past him, and when we were nearly nose-to-nose he said, 'Why do I want to have sex with every woman I meet?' I discussed the incident with my female consultant supervisor, and she said he did it to her too. If we reported it to the prison staff, the payback was likely to be a refusal to collect prisoners for our clinic, so it was better not to say anything. I certainly wouldn't have given the same advice to one of my trainees. I'd like to think that prisons are less macho nowadays, with policies and procedures in place to deal with this type of harassment. But there's still the issue of needing to know that colleagues will have your back during an incident and a fear that whistleblowing may potentially leave staff in a vulnerable position.

CHAPTER 14

Facing Sherlock

I hadn't been a senior registrar in psychiatry for long when I was asked to be an expert witness in a murder trial. It all started while I was doing my routine prison clinic at HMP Cornton Vale, the national female prison. The next name on my list that day was unknown to me but apparently this young woman was on remand for murder and there wasn't much doubt that she'd killed the victim. Everyone remanded on a charge of murder is routinely seen by two psychiatric experts, instructed by the procurator fiscal (the prosecutor) before they are allowed to plead to the charges, to make sure they're sane and fit to plead. Needless to say, over the years I've seen many murderers for this purpose. The overwhelming majority haven't been mentally ill. If you plead guilty to a charge of murder, there's no need for a trial and you're given a mandatory life sentence. It causes problems if the offender doesn't understand the legal process, legal options and the consequences of each plea. If there's clear evidence that they killed the victim, they may believe they have no alternative but to plead guilty to murder.

In Scotland, there's an alternative charge of culpable

homicide, which effectively means that you killed the victim but didn't have intent to kill. A good example of this might be in the context of domestic violence, where the wife is attacked while chopping onions, tries to defend herself and accidentally slashes her partner in the neck, causing him to bleed out from his carotid artery and die. She may have called 999 for an ambulance immediately, and there was no intent to kill or attempt to conceal her actions. Here there may be grounds for a plea of self-defence and the charge may be culpable homicide. If convicted of culpable homicide, the disposal options can vary from probation to life imprisonment. However, if the distraught wife is asked if she murdered her husband she might say yes. If that's the case, then these options wouldn't be available, hence the need to check that she's mentally well enough to understand these matters and appear in court before being allowed to plead to the charge.

This expert assessment is also the first opportunity to highlight whether or not the accused may have been suffering from a mental illness at the time of the crime, as the court should be alerted to a psychiatric defence at the earliest opportunity. A crime thought to be driven directly by mental illness would affect where the prisoner would be remanded for assessment (i.e. a secure hospital rather than a prison environment). Consideration needs to be given to possible defences, the ability to understand court process, fitness to plead, fitness to stand trial, and potential court disposal options if convicted. Contrary to the procurator fiscal's duty to disclose, the defence legal team can instruct their own psychiatric expert, but if they think the opinion isn't helpful to their client, they can choose not to share it with the court. This has never sat well with me, as a person who may have had mental health issues picked up by the defence psychiatrist may go unreported and untreated.

Back at the prison clinic, the nurses told me that this prisoner had refused to cooperate with the two expert psychiatrists who'd attended to assess her fitness to plead. The nurses were concerned about her mental health. If I could get her to understand the importance of talking to someone about the different charges, pleas and consequences thereof, she may revisit her decision not to cooperate. My role was not court related; I was simply the prison psychiatrist offering support to those women incarcerated within our walls.

Somewhat surprisingly, I gained her trust and she started to open up to me. As the interview progressed, she wanted to talk about the crime, which in my limited experience was quite unusual for a prisoner remanded on a murder charge, as their lawyers often advise them not to discuss the crime in case they incriminate themselves. The young woman described feeling acutely distressed as the altercation with the victim had triggered flashbacks of her own childhood experiences. She spontaneously described things around her feeling small, muffled and unreal as well as feeling emotionally detached from the situation. Her recollection of events was patchy, but she admitted to stabbing him multiple times before leaving.

There was no doubt in my mind that she'd killed him, but I thought her behavioural response may have been influenced by post-traumatic stress symptoms linked to previous trauma, plus depersonalisation, derealisation and dissociation, linked to acute stress. Depersonalisation is the experience of feeling detached from, and as if you're an outside observer of, your mental processes, body or actions. Derealisation refers to the experience of feeling detached from, and as if you're an outside observer of, your surroundings. They can be triggered by stress, may result in significant impairment of functioning and may be described as feeling detached. Dissociative disorders are conditions that involve descriptions of breakdown of memory, awareness, identity or perception. Dissociation is an involuntary defence mechanism used to protect ourselves and can be triggered by psychological trauma. I didn't think she had a mental illness like schizophrenia, but advised her to contact her lawyer and explain that the prison psychiatrist advised that the defence should consider requesting an expert opinion. What she was describing may be helpful to her defence. As I wasn't an expert, I didn't expect the lawyer to instruct me. But here I was, just in the door, with a title but little experience to speak of, heading for my first murder trial as an expert witness. It turned out that another forensic psychiatrist had been instructed as well. And she had about 30 years of experience under her belt.

The court day arrived. The lawyer waltzed in in his robes, announcing that my esteemed, experienced colleague would be called to give evidence first and then it would be my turn. With stomach churning and heart pounding, I nervously read and re-read my psychiatric report to ensure I was clear about my evidence. Court cases always took place many months after the assessment, so often weren't fresh in your mind. As an added pressure, Donald Findlay QC was going to be questioning me. He was incredibly well known nationally. A regular in the press, he'd been involved in many high-profile murder trials. He was known for his intimidating questioning style and appearance, with large sideburns and curvy pipe, almost a caricature of Sherlock Holmes.

'Dr Morrison, please.'

What? They were supposed to be calling me up second! What followed was an excruciating courtroom debut. As sweat trickled down my back and my heart thudded against my chest wall, I desperately tried to maintain my outward composure. But then he asked, 'How long have you been a forensic psychiatrist, Dr Morrison?' I sensed 'a few months' wasn't likely to increase my credibility. And I knew who was coming next.

What followed is now a fractured, traumatic memory. I was trying to convey to Sherlock that, in my opinion, acute anxiety, depersonalisation, derealisation and dissociation, triggered by re-traumatisation, may have contributed to the defendant's abnormal state of mind, judgement and behavioural response at the time of the offence. I can share it here because the information about the case is in the public domain. As I remember it, the forensic evidence confirmed she'd strangled the victim to death. The multiple stab wounds had been inflicted post mortem. If she'd gone round to the house with intent to kill, it seemed unlikely that she'd have planned to strangle him. But what did I know?! Fortunately, it wasn't my job to comment on that. Her symptoms might be useful for a possible diminished responsibility defence. Sherlock wanted me to say 'a state bordering on but not amounting to insanity' at the time of the offence, but the legal terminology felt alien to me. The term insanity is not used by psychiatrists. Her symptoms certainly weren't equivalent to acute psychosis, which might be the closest equivalent in our terminology. I was in the witness stand for what seemed like days, but in reality it was a few hours. It didn't matter how many times he rephrased the question; I just didn't feel able to use the terminology as it didn't seem to fit what I was trying to describe. I preferred to describe her symptoms. Eventually I was excused. It was not my finest hour.

I stayed in court to hear my colleague's evidence. She answered Sherlock's questions exactly as he wanted them to be answered and was done and dusted in about 20 minutes. I quickly realised that I preferred working directly with mentally disordered offenders to playing the game in court, which relies on showmanship, plays on words and, if the evidence doesn't support their client's case, attempts to discredit expert witnesses. Working at the coal face with mentally disordered offenders in the community felt like a more honest and rewarding pursuit. This was my destiny. I did get better at preparing expert reports for the court, but I didn't seek them out. The outmoded terminology referencing insanity would eventually be replaced with the need for the accused to lack criminal responsibility by reason of mental disorder at the time of the offence, which would've meant they were unable to appreciate the wrongfulness of their conduct.

CHAPTER 15

No Machete Next Time, Please

B ack at the Douglas Inch clinic, my new patient acknowl-edged me without making eye contact. I asked him if he knew why his GP had referred him, then noticed the sleeve of his anorak. It was big and bulky, and he couldn't bend his arm because of it. I tried not to register my alarm. I took my heart out of my mouth and weighed up my options. The referral letter, as with many of my outpatients, mentioned drug misuse, paranoia, history of violence and anger management problems. I've always believed that, if you want to gain someone's trust, honesty's the best policy, even if the message is difficult. This is how our exchange went.

'I notice you've got something down the sleeve of your anorak. I'm wondering if it's a weapon? I don't want to get you into trouble, and it won't affect me seeing you. I just need to ensure that we're both safe during the appointment. Can you tell me what it is?'

'A machete.'

'Why have you brought a machete to your outpatient appointment?'

'I dinnae feel safe walking aboot. I need it tae protect ma'sel.'

'If I'm going to work with you on your anger, it's possible we may cover some issues that trigger these emotions. I won't feel safe doing that if you get angry and have a machete with you. Can you promise that you won't bring it to future appointments? I don't want to get hurt and I don't want you to get into trouble.'

He grunted and nodded. Phew.

Over the course of my career, I would encounter many patients who felt the need to carry weapons for protection, whether due to paranoid delusions, drug debts, a recent assault, living in a gang-dominated environment or simply to maintain their reputation within the gang culture. Whatever the motivation, it was a no-no in my clinic. People with mental health problems live in a context, which will inevitably influence how they present. Often there are repeated missed appointments and occasional precipitous endings when angry patients storm out of the room. We may have negotiated that they should leave if they start to become angry. Attendance gradually improves and trust begins to develop. Little by little, a scowling skinhead may share snippets of his history. Anger, paranoia, mood swings, suicidal thoughts, a collection of weapons, drug misuse and violence may all feature. The one thing I never did was jump to a discharge letter for non-attendance. Trust was so fragile with my patients and some of their lives so chaotic that I wasn't going to reject them. Their behaviour had often generated a self-fulfilling prophecy regarding rejection... but not with me. I wasn't playing that game. I recall one patient who reappeared after a lengthy absence, smiling for the first time. My previously intimidating, surly outpatient was chatty and upbeat. A breakthrough? I was intrigued.

'Good to see you. Nice to see you smiling. What's been happening?'

'I had one of my black moods for a few weeks and then I woke up last week and looked out the window. It was as if the world was in technicolour, and I felt really happy. I could see the flowers and all the different colours. I felt great. I went fishing.'

You could've knocked me down with a feather. He'd been drug-free for a while and here was the first evidence that he may have been experiencing an underlying mood disorder, previously masked by antisocial behaviour, drug misuse, personality disorder and repeated non-attendance at clinic. It had been worth the wait and hanging on in there. Now we could look at treatment. This case taught me an important lesson. Openness, honesty and sticking power are vital components of forensic care, as is a non-judgemental attitude. We often had to repair the damage caused by previous authority figures in patients' lives. The process towards gaining their trust could be a long one. If I believed someone was genuinely unwell, I didn't always adhere to the health board's outpatient policy, which was to discharge patients for repeated non-attendance. Many of our patients weren't good at contacting us when they were remanded in custody or chucked out of the house by their girlfriend, and were even worse at jumping through hoops to get re-referred. Keeping them on the books and fitting them in when they resurfaced was much more responsive and efficient. Routine appointments didn't tend to coincide with periods of calm within the chaos of their existence. Once we'd got them hooked, we had a chance of building a therapeutic relation-ship. I managed my own diary to ensure that I could respond flexibly in a crisis, organise urgent home visits and avoid having a waiting list.

As my career progressed, I started to notice a recurrent pattern of behaviour in patients who'd had difficult childhood experiences, which included inconsistent parenting or abuse of trust by authority figures. They'd come to believe that it was not safe to trust authority figures, believing they'd ultimately let them down or reject them. What I went on to witness was my patients being slow to trust me, constantly testing boundaries and often actively behaving in a way that would encourage me to reject them or discharge them from services. This would in some way reinforce their existing belief system and mean they weren't putting themselves in the position of trusting me and then being rejected. It gave them some control but meant that a continuous cycle of negative relationships would develop. I decided not to engage. I set clear boundaries regarding acceptable behaviour, but pursued the path less trodden. I kept sending appointments and tried to assist with a range of issues, often not directly related to treatment of their mental health problem, e.g. housing, social, substance misuse and financial challenges.

It took a while, but eventually they started to realise that we weren't going to discharge them for a few missed appointments and would respond quickly in a crisis. A glimmer of trust would eventually emerge. My patients didn't always fall into the category of people who are organised enough to have an appointment calendar. Some were sofa-surfing or locked up in police cells over the weekend and had no money left on their mobile phone, so contacting us to say that they might not make their appointment wasn't always straightforward. Later on, when I was a consultant, I used gaps in the outpatient clinic list to do impromptu additional training for my junior doctor or nurses attending the clinic. However, the patients sometimes just rocked up to the clinic on the wrong day, expecting to be seen.

With a client group like mine, I rarely had to worry about receiving gifts. I was always told not to accept gifts from patients that were of any value, as it may be viewed as unethical and blur the professional boundary, particularly if the person had been seen for a court report and accepting the gift could be misconstrued as a bribe. I was more likely to receive threats. I was once sent a knife in a Jiffy bag and one woman went berserk in my first-floor office, attempting to launch the bookcase out of the window. I was glad to be near the door. I exited and called the police before going back into the room with a police escort to talk her down.

However, one day the receptionist phoned through to say a patient had popped in to leave a gift. Intrigued, I went round to pick it up. It was a single, limp daffodil, plucked from the planter outside, left by an intoxicated patient who'd failed to turn up for the group programme. It made me smile. My next gift came from an unlikely source, as I'd seen the gentleman for a one-off court report assessment. He'd returned a week later with a large box of fruit and veg and left it at reception. This was much more expensive. We are talking about a dozen bananas, six apples, six oranges, a melon, a large pineapple, grapes, carrots, and so on. I discussed with my supervisor whether it could be construed as a bribe. I'd already submitted my report before receiving the gift and couldn't give it back. The produce would go to waste if not used. In the end we concluded it hadn't influenced my opinion and I shared it with the clinic staff. As a result of my previous experience of psychotherapy supervision, I avoided the bananas.

Relationships with patients who've been on the outpatient caseload for many years are very different and the issue of gifts can be more complicated. They often develop emotional attachments and a degree of dependence, as we may see them more often than their own family. They may experience their discharge or the doctor retiring as a form of rejection, so these occasions require sensitive management. A failure to accept a thank-you gift could have a devastating impact. But all the thanks I needed was to know I'd positively impacted their lives, or to have seen their illness stabilise and watched them succeed, despite their illness. I did go on to receive some tasteful gifts from a small group of long-term patients at the end of my career, which I still cherish.

Chapter 16

Have You Had the Stroke Talk Yet?

Fortunately, I've rarely been a customer of the NHS, but my limited experience has been variable. Shortly before Vivienne died, we'd discovered by accident that she might have an inherited bleeding disorder. No other member of the family had been tested. Maybe, I thought, this would explain my menorrhagia (heavy periods). At the haematology clinic for bleeding disorders at Glasgow Royal Infirmary, testing involved being stabbed in the arm with two small knives and timing how long it took for the blood to stop flowing out of my arm. Highly technical! After oozing blood for 21 minutes, I was told I might have it. In a review of my sister's case notes, the disorder was mentioned by name, but the diagnosis was never confirmed. So, they changed their minds about my bleeding time results, which was highly unsatisfactory as it didn't explain the abnormality. Preferring not to be labelled neurotic, it remained parked as a doubt in my mind, to be revisited if I ever got pregnant or needed an operation. Therefore, before I gave birth to my first baby and potentially bled out on the table, I had to be retested. More knives! This time they arrived at a more conclusive decision that my bleeding time was fine. However, I now have a series of scars on my right forearm which make me look as if I've self-harmed. It's not a good look for a psychiatrist.

I'm aware of the stigma that can be caused by scarring associated with previous self-laceration. One of my patients had extensive scarring to both forearms from deliberate self-harm. When in recovery and doing well, they felt more stigmatised by the scarring than their diagnosis, especially in the summer when their arms were bare. I contacted the cosmetic surgeons to ask if they could help. After considerable negotiation and an 18-month period free from self-harm, they skin-grafted my patient's forearm. Then, 18 months later, they did the other arm. The skin grafts were noticeable too, but looked like burns rather than the less socially acceptable scars from self-harming. Skin grafts are not normally listed as treatment options in psychiatry, but this is a good example of person-centred care because it really mattered to my patient.

Later in my career one of the NHS initiatives was to introduce 'What matters to you?' as a routine question. It was long overdue. If staff ask this question, a patient's care will be more person centred. Someone in hospital who's dying of cancer might prefer contact with their dog rather than yet another course of toxic chemotherapy that might make them feel sick. That might be what matters to them. But let's get back to the blood test. After that, my pregnancy progressed uneventfully until the latter stages, when I developed pre-eclampsia (high blood pressure, protein in the urine, fluid retention). I was like a beached whale and had to buy size eight slippers because my swollen feet were hanging over my shoes. At 38 weeks I was admitted to hospital due to high blood pressure, with a diastolic BP recording of 110. It should have been 70. Pregnant mothers shared their war stories in the sitting room.

'Have you had the stroke talk yet?'

'My blood pressure is so high that they said I could have a stroke, so I'm having my baby tomorrow.'

I wasn't getting the stroke talk or the baby tomorrow; I was just in for monitoring. Was I getting a second-rate service? Was I going to have a stroke? My hormones and emotions were all over the place. Because I was a patient who was also a doctor, the nurses avoided me. I'd been admitted for hourly BP monitoring from the day hospital at lunchtime. It was now midnight, and my BP hadn't been checked. I approached the nurse's station in tears and eventually had it checked. Still high. No reassurance there, then. A few days in, and several ultrasound scans later, I had a visit from the senior registrar.

I asked, 'When am I going to have my baby? Am I going to get a caesarean section?'

He replied, 'We'll try to induce you.'

Several hours later, everything down below was shut for business and the scans were showing steadily reducing fluid around the baby, which wasn't a good sign. I moved it up a gear.

'Can you tell the consultant that if he doesn't section me, I'm sectioning him and he's going to Carstairs!?' I was only half joking!

The threat of detention in a high-security hospital seemed to work and we were soon off to theatre. He decided on a spinal anaesthetic, so I'd be frozen from the waist down but awake to watch the delivery. Richard gowned up and came into the operating theatre. He was delighted. He'd patiently listened to my tales of surgery and was a bit jealous. Now he was having his own adventure. To my horror, when they started to cut me open, I could feel them cutting, pulling and tugging the baby out. I hadn't realised the anaesthetic would knock out the pain receptors but not the other senses. For a split second I thought it hadn't worked and I was having an operation without an anaesthetic. I nearly passed out. There was the added compli-cation of the date: Friday 13th. What on earth were they going to haul out of my gaping wound?

It was a beautiful baby girl. We named her Jill. My other suggestion, Judy, was bombed out by several family members, mimicking Punch and Judy in puppet show voices. We were so proud; she was perfect. Having a baby with no labour was clearly the way to go. Breastfeeding was more of a challenge and took several days to master. A breast abscess was the icing on the motherhood cake. Mum had brainwashed me that dummies were dirty and I shouldn't use them. I struggled on womanfully, trying to feed her myself. She had colic, screamed a lot and wouldn't latch on properly, gulping more air than milk, which didn't help. Days later, while sitting on the toilet in our small en-suite bathroom, I felt something give. Fluid spurted out of a small section of my inflamed but healing scar and hit the wall in front of me. My C-section wound had burst! Eventually all of the fluid drained away and the wound healed, but my ruptured scar would come back to haunt me.

My only other encounters with the health service came later in life when I paid to go private. It didn't sit well with me as an NHS doctor, but I wasn't prepared to wait for 42 weeks to have neurological investigations for a cluster of episodes of visual disturbance. I was seeing arcs of zigzag lines, which made my visual field look as if someone had been let loose with pinking shears. I knew that visual disturbance could occur with migraine headaches, but I had no headache symptoms and was now 40. This was completely new. I didn't want to wait that long for reassurance or to find out too late that I had a brain tumour. The next time was when I found a hard lump under my arm, most likely a lymph node. In the absence of any infection to explain it, I automatically thought of breast cancer, as two close friends of a similar age had been treated for it. The examination, diagnosis and treatment service for suspected breast cancer is usually prompt, but I was so worried that I asked for a private appointment, which I got within two days. At a one-stop-shop clinic I had the consultation, examination, mammography and lymph node biopsy. Result: all clear. It was worth the money.

Then, as I approached the menopause, I had to cope with excessive bleeding. When it resumed after a course of medication, I was sent back to the gynaecologist. I'd been told that I'd require a general anaesthetic for the next procedure, and believed I was going in to discuss the timing of the operation. To my surprise, the consultant lay me on the couch, put my legs in stirrups and announced she'd do the procedure there and then. During the procedure, she chatted about my job and her own experience of forensic psychiatry during her training, discussing a case where someone had dismembered a body and put it in bin bags. It certainly provided a welcome distraction...

CHAPTER 17

Hurdles Practice

It was Boxing Day 1991. We were at home with Jill, aged three months. I was in the shower when the telephone rang. Richard answered. It was Mum, panicking: 'John's not breathing. I can't get the doctor on the phone.' Mum had come in from the garden to find Dad unresponsive in the armchair. It was a public holiday, and she was having trouble getting through to the emergency GP or ambulance service. Naked and dripping wet, I gave Mum instructions over the phone about how to administer CPR (cardio–pulmonary resuscitation), which is not something I thought I'd ever have to do: 'I'll call the ambulance. You just keep pressing on his chest and breathe into his mouth like I told you, till they come. Richard's on his way down.' Having called the ambulance, I needed to get dressed. Then I needed to get to Dad. Thoughts swirled around my head. 'Is he going to make it? He can't have died; I'm only 28. What to wear?' I'd just had a baby and still looked pregnant. Richard had bought me a lilac-patterned sweater for Christmas, which was in the pile of presents beside the bed. That would have to do. I'm embarrassed to admit it, but badminton players all owned shell suits at that time, and I had a lilac one. I pulled it on. It was tight. No time to worry about that.

I grabbed Jill, strapped her into her car seat and we were off. 'Oh God, is this it?' I didn't know what to expect at the other end.

I arrived 15 minutes later. The street was busy, with an ambulance parked awkwardly outside the house. Neighbours and children were treating the whole incident as festive entertainment and were standing in the street, watching in anticipation. I abandoned my car, with Jill still strapped in her car seat, and ran to the house. I could think of nothing else but getting to my dad. The wrought iron gate and path that led to the front door were a few yards to the right of my car. The shortest route as the crow flies was straight over a foot-high privet hedge. I cleared the hedge but, like a horse pulling up in the Grand National, the lilac shell suit refused. I landed flat out on the muddy winter grass, having hit my hand on the concrete path in the process. My lilac ensemble was now smeared with mud and my hand was cut and bleeding. Off I stumbled into the house, dignity abandoned on the lawn.

'Where's Dad?'

My mother's red-rimmed eyes and the hand on my shoulder said it all. Dad hadn't made it. He'd been laid out on his bed, so I went up to sit with him. He was wearing his favourite patterned jumper, with a familiar stale tobacco smell, looking as if he were sleeping. My sister Elaine had arrived before the GP or ambulance and had taken over the CPR from Mum. I could hear her sobbing in the kitchen below. I ended up being the one who was treated by the doctor for my injuries. I don't think I processed it at the time. When I think back to that day I always smile because of the ridiculous hurdling incident and the doctor having to administer first aid. Dad died the way I would like to go, quickly and painlessly. It was hard, because we didn't get to prepare for it or say goodbye, but it was better for him. On reflection, I think I forged a coping strategy for life at that moment. Twinning humour or a positive thought with a difficult incident seems to soften the memory. I loved my dad; he was a good man and he's in a better place.

Richard's dad had died earlier that year after a heart-breaking diagnosis of metastatic lung cancer. It was sad to see such a lovely man become a shadow of his former self. We were all there and got to say goodbye, but it had been hard to watch his decline. Richard was proud to have been able to tell his dad before he died that I was six weeks pregnant. He was the first to know and was delighted. We thought he might not remember because of the morphine, but he proved us wrong, having told all of the nurses the news. Fortunately, my dad got to meet Jill and attended her christening a few days before he died, but she'd never get to know what a great man he was. The week before, he'd also witnessed her surprise appearance as baby Jesus at the carol service. Having agreed to christen Jill, the minister had then asked a favour. I was to be dressed as Mary, with Jill in swaddling clothes, and we'd be entering the church during 'Away in a Manger' as a surprise for the congregation and her grandparents. She made an angelic Jesus, preferring to keep her colicky screams and vomiting on my jacket for the christening service a week later.

I was overwhelmed by the hundreds of people who attended Dad's funeral and the heartfelt eulogy delivered by Reverend Haughton. It was overwhelming to be walking down the aisle again so soon, this time to say our goodbyes to Dad. To compare my dad to the Good Samaritan was the ultimate compliment. He was a quiet, unassuming man who made a positive impact on all who knew him.

Funerals are strange affairs. Should we be sad, mourning a life that has ended, or should they be a celebration of a life well lived? I guess I'm more in favour of celebrating life. Death is like a bookmark at the end of a chapter, an inevitability for everyone. It's what we choose to achieve while we're here that matters. I have a 'no regrets' mentality. I believe that if you want to do something, you should just go for it. I tried to instil that in my patients, too. You may have to cope with illness or disability, but it doesn't have to define you or prevent you from enjoying a fulfilling life.

I felt guilty going back to work when Jill was only four months old, but I was the main breadwinner. We employed a fantastic nursery nurse called Vivienne as our nanny (a coincidence?) and Jill thrived. Vivvie number two had a baby a year later, but was so good that we kept her on, and she just brought her baby with her as a playmate for Jill. My manager was hopeful of securing funding to create a new consultant post in forensic learning disability psychiatry, so my training was extended. To allow me to apply, I'd expressed an interest in completing dual speciality training. It would've allowed me to get back to my original game plan, forged during my days at Lennox Castle visiting Vivienne. During this period, I did return to Lennox Castle for some forensic learning disability experience. It was odd going back there as a psychiatrist, having known the culture in the wards when I was a summer student nursing assistant and visitor.

I also co-ran a group at Douglas Inch for sex offenders with a learning disability. We were addressing deficits in sexual education and social skills training. Often the offenders had been protected by families who were too worried about their vulnerable teenager to talk about these matters. However, teenagers experience hormonal changes, sexual arousal and have an interest in relationships whether they have a learning disability or not. Without any knowledge about how to behave, they sometimes found themselves on the wrong side of the law. There were some hilarious sessions during which a colleague and I gave 'chat-up' demos and demonstrated how to use a condom. I once had to deliver a presentation to colleagues after my HIV counselling training, involving a collection of ribbed and flavoured condoms acquired from the local clinic. The cleaner probably had a bit of a shock when she emptied the meeting room bin that day. The reward for completing attendance at our group for sex offenders with a learning disability was a Christmas lunch in a local Indian restaurant funded by the senior registrars facilitating the group. Here the group could practise their newly acquired social skills. Let's just say it was a long, awkward lunch.

CHAPTER 18

The Art of Jigsaws

In 1996, while pregnant with my second child, I was appointed to my first post as a consultant forensic psychiatrist. I'd achieved dual accreditation in forensic and general adult psychiatry. They never did find funding in time for me to pursue forensic learning disability, but created a new post for me in NHS Forth Valley that involved general psychiatry, intensive care psychiatry and prison psychiatry at Cornton Vale. As a consultant I was expected to train junior psychiatrists and senior trainees. To manage expectations when meeting a new trainee doctor, I always started with a confession: 'I believe there are different ways to practise psychiatry. In my head there's dot-to-dot psychiatry, where you stick to strict diagnostic guidelines and treatments that guide you through diagnosis and care planning, like dot-to-dot painting. Then there's the art of psychiatry, which probably describes my style. I tried dot-to-dot psychiatry, but along the way multiple patients didn't quite meet the diagnostic criteria outlined in ICD10 and DSM-4 manuals and didn't always respond to recommended treatment and medication. Do we run out of dots and let patients suffer, or do we treat the individual? I view patients rather like jigsaws. First you have to turn over all the pieces, make sure you can see the details on each piece, and then assemble them to form the final version. If there are any damaged pieces, we try to fix them together.'

Understanding the detail of each patient's picture is essentially about taking a good history, and that requires the ability to engage with them enough to tell their story. This is the crucial skill. In forensic psychiatry, the risk factors are likely to be the damaged pieces of the jigsaw, which we need to fix or manage in order to reduce the risk. Small improvements in several areas of risk can make a big difference to the overall risk jigsaw and quality of life. At its most basic level, the art of psychiatry is about obtaining the history. As a junior psychiatrist, I was taught to ask about the presenting complaint, then the history of the presenting complaint, and then take the background history. In forensic psychiatry, the presenting complaint is usually the offence. If you plough into talking about the offence first, you do so at your peril. The lawyer has probably told their client not to talk to anyone about it and not to admit anything in order to avoid incriminating themselves.

Many of my patients had a personality disorder as well as mental illness, plus possible substance misuse. I often heard nursing colleagues describe their behaviour as manipulative. I hated that word. If anyone was a good manipulator, it was me. If I could get them to disclose details about their use of weapons, offending, substance misuse and anti-authoritarian attitude without realising that they might be incriminating themselves, I had a chance to properly assess and manage their risk. If I could persuade a violent, psychotic man to give me the weapon, not to hit me, do a drugs screen, accept the injection of antipsychotic medication every fortnight and tell me who he was planning to stab, then I guess I was a good manipulator. I could sell a chocolate fireguard. It was all about how to frame your questions and requests.

In addition to the art I mentioned earlier, honesty is always the best policy. Let's take the hypothetical example of an offender who's been charged with possession of drugs and a violent stabbing of a policeman. I need to know if he usually carries weapons, uses drugs and is anti-authoritarian. If I ask him outright, he may deny all of it. Over the years I found that the art of getting this information relates to how and when you ask the question. This is what I would say: 'I plan to start from when you were a wee boy, then work up to more recent times and the offence. That way I get to understand more about you as a person, what has happened in your life that might be important, and then we'll discuss what happened last. Does that make sense?' The usual response was 'Yes'. When the offence was left until last, they were immediately caught off guard.

We were always taught to start with open questions and avoid leading the patient – for example: 'Tell me about your schooling.' In forensic psychiatry, I had an extensive list of direct follow-up questions. In my experience, if you asked, they told you; if you didn't, they gave you the most socially acceptable answer and no more. It was a game. In the hypothetical example, I'd have a particular focus on relationships with authority figures while they were growing up and how their behaviour towards the offender may have impacted personality development and attitude – for example, the impact of abuse of trust, excessive discipline, loss, abandonment and violence. I'd give real-time examples and watch the reaction, saying, 'If a teacher or the police say sit down and shut up [while I am pointing in their face], what would you do? Would you sit down, or would you tell them to f*** off?' They could never resist responding honestly. I'd push their anti-authoritarian button by asking, 'How do you cope with rules?' If they were anti-authoritarian, the response was usually very clear, something along the lines of 'I hate f***ing rules!'

When taking their education history, I also asked about truancy: 'What did you do when you were truanting from school? Did you try drugs and alcohol? Did you offend? Were you ever in a gang?' These more direct questions tended to elicit more information than my colleagues would obtain if they stopped at an open question. I'd follow up on the answers later, but the gang question would be followed up immediately: 'Did you ever have to carry weapons for protection?' The 'for protection' part was deliberate. Most offenders went no further than the socially acceptable response unless pressed (and I always pressed). Saying 'for protection' made it feel legitimate. If they said yes, I pursued the question. Often, they said 'a knife' and I followed up with a more direct pick-and-mix list. The answer often expanded to include swords, golf clubs, machetes or baseball bats. It was important to ask. They might become my patient in the community and require a home visit. Forewarned is forearmed: 'Have you ever had to use them? What's the worst injury to have happened as a result?' By this point, while we were still in the early life and education section, we may have established that they were anti-author-itarian, carried weapons and were experimenting with drugs and alcohol at the age of 13, which was useful to know before we got to the 'presenting complaint' when they might try to deny everything.

Sometimes doctors fall into traps too. When asked if everything discussed is confidential, inexperienced doctors often reply 'Of course'. Alarm bells should be ringing and red flags appearing out of their ears at that point. In my experience, patients only ever ask about confidentiality before they tell you something you can't keep confidential and have a duty to report, thus potentially breaching confidentiality. We have a duty to our patients but also to protect the public. One day, I was met in the corridor by a flustered-looking trainee psychia-trist, who asked for some urgent advice. She wasn't my trainee, so I guessed it couldn't wait for her supervision session. She'd just seen a patient who'd asked the confidentiality question. Having reassured him regarding confidentiality, he'd then disclosed to her that he'd hidden a weapon in the cemetery and had plans to kill his neighbour. The patient had subsequently left the appointment, leaving a highly distressed doctor in his wake. We'd have to get the patient back in, involve the police and retrieve the weapon, as a named victim was at risk.

After an awkward telephone call (during which she told the patient she'd discussed the case in supervision and forgotten to ask a few questions, so could he come back in to meet the consultant in the afternoon), we reconvened to gain more information and explain to the patient our duty to disclose, our desire to keep him from offending, and to keep his named victim safe. We also explained that we needed to contact the police in order to retrieve the weapon, as carrying a weapon in a public place is an offence, so he couldn't just go and get it and hand it in. Armed with the facts, he cooperated. On more than one occasion, I had to report patients to the police due to the possession of guns and threats to kill. Interestingly, they respected me for my honesty and the rationale behind my actions, and continued to engage with me. Setting boundaries and being consistent are part of the art of psychiatry too, as ultimately patients know where they stand with you and trust starts to build. The downside of reporting these matters was that the police often sent someone out to my house to take a statement, which left me wondering if I was the guilty party. Goodness knows what the neighbours thought.

By this point, baby number two was late, and attempts to induce him were not working. A decision was made for me to have a caesarean section under spinal anaesthesia, and I asked if the screen could be left down so I could watch. It wasn't one of my wisest decisions. When they cut me open, they disturbed my old scar and the wound burst. All I could see were several concerned doctors speaking in low tones at the foot of the operating table. I was preoccupied with my baby boy, so I didn't understand what was happening. Back in the ward, the doctor came to explain: 'Your wound burst open because of the scar tissue and limited blood supply. We're worried about how the wound will heal, so we've cobbled you together with huge stitches, rather than the usual clips, to try to hold everything together. A catheter has been left in place because we think we may have nicked your bladder.' This was getting worse by the minute. And it was about to get even worse.

'You won't be able to have any more children. Your uterus won't survive another pregnancy.'

'How long will it be before you can book me in for a sterilisation operation?'

'We're not going to risk opening you up again. Your husband should get something done instead.'

I let all that sink in before I called Richard.

Then the paediatric senior registrar arrived. 'Hello, just here to check the baby. His hips are fine. He seems quite alert. Oh, and he seems to have a heart murmur. He might have a ventricular septal defect, a hole in his heart. We'll get him back for an echocardiogram in about a month. He might need heart surgery.'

Oh my god! I had to process that for a minute...

'I had my baby in the maternity hospital next to the sick children's hospital for a reason, so that if there was anything wrong, it would be dealt with immediately.'

I wasn't going anywhere until he'd had an echocardiogram. I think they sensed my anguish, so the echocardiogram was arranged, and off we went for the scan of our tiny baby's heart. He looked so vulnerable lying there in his nappy.

'Yes, he has a VSD. He'll probably need heart surgery.'

You never know when your university pals will come in handy. William's big brother was the paediatric heart surgeon at the children's hospital.

'William, if he needs surgery will you get your brother to do it? I don't trust anyone else.'

'I'll speak to him.'

In the end, my intervention wasn't necessary. At the one-month follow-up, the hole in Fraser's heart had closed by itself, which is often the case. Fortunately, we'd never planned on having a big family, so being forced to stop at two because of surgical risk was not too devastating for either of us. When I discussed it with Richard, he agreed to have a vasectomy. As with most things in life, he was practical about it.

CHAPTER 19

That's My Baby

I only have two children, but I've given birth three times. The third was the creation of the forensic community mental health team at Forth Valley, one of the greatest achievements of my medical career. It was the first of its kind in Scotland, and we were later awarded runner-up in the UK Hospital Doctor Psychiatry Team of the Year awards, which was such a proud moment for me. When setting up the team, the group interview process we designed for nurse appointments proved to be inspired. We observed as the applicants completed the task of planning a court liaison scheme, noting the leaders, the team players, the compromisers and the ideas people. Each of them then gave a short presentation on one aspect of the service they'd designed, and there were individual interviews in the afternoon.

Sixteen years later, the team still had its original line-up, apart from one nurse who died far too young. People who passed through our team commented on how experienced, skilled and welcoming our nurses were. Trainees often came back to work with us, which was testament to a super group of individuals. We were a sociable bunch: we celebrated birthdays, had monthly payday lunches, invited each other to weddings and had an annual Christmas party. When my fellow consultant and one of the nurses turned 40, we travelled abroad for a double birthday celebration. I was told I needed to attend, no arguments. So, we headed to Benidorm for our three-night, all-inclusive Christmas/birthday bash, complete with sparkly cowboy hats, fake tan, Irn-Bru WKD and a planned trip to see Sticky Vicky (I didn't sign up for that particular excursion, having no interest in seeing someone firing ping-pong balls from between their legs!). At our team murder mystery celebration, there were sheriffs, saloon girls in basques and feather boas, Indian chiefs in full headdresses, an undertaker who measured our bodies for coffins during lunch, and a cavalryman, played by my higher trainee. His costume suggestion card mentioned long black boots, which he didn't own. Not wanting to be seen as a party pooper, he taped black bin bags round his legs, right up to his knees. I've never let him forget it. The service manager, playing a cowboy, rode around on a hobby horse that neighed when you pressed its ear. It was a sight to behold during the working day and provided light relief from the day-to-day stresses of our work.

It's hard to pinpoint the special qualities of our team, but we certainly went the extra mile for our patients in an attempt to build trust and respect. The buzzwords in psychiatry at the time included holistic, person-centred, recovery-focused and trauma-informed care. Our staff embodied all of that in their interactions with patients. When one of our nurses discovered that her new patient had no cooker or carpets, a poor quality of life and no trusting relationships, she turned up with a microwave and homemade beef olives. She didn't just care about his antipsychotic medication and the Mental Health Act; she cared about him and was able to see the person behind the label of 'mentally disordered offender'. Months later, he came to the clinic and told me he thought he'd had a relapse. Having heard my voice coming from his living room, he'd crept in there anxiously, only to find me actually talking on the TV. We laughed about it together.

We supported another patient at the hospice during his partner's palliative care. You might think that this work could've been carried out by a lower-paid support worker, but you'd be missing the point. Engaging potentially violent, paranoid patients who are anti-authoritarian and lacking in trust was our bread and butter. If we could engage them at a human level and truly demonstrate that we were non-judgemental, we could go on to have those difficult conversations more safely when we hit a boundary. It helped when we had to report them to the police for possessing a weapon and having a named victim, or needed to get them to hospital when they were unwell and it was too unsafe for them to remain in the community.

Another outpatient announced to me that he'd heard command hallucinations the previous evening, despite being on medication.

'They told me to stab you.'

I felt panicky but managed to maintain a calm facade, channelling my inner swan: serene on the surface, legs paddling frantically under the water. I checked to see if I had a clear route to the door just in case I needed to make a quick exit.

'Are the voices still there?'

'Don't be daft, I wouldn't have come if they were!'

What a relief to discover he had insight. That was the sort of thing that happened in my outpatient clinic. I relied on the team to manage fluctuating risk by cranking up a gear at a moment's notice. Our social work colleagues often tried to manage limited resources by allocating staff to deal with crises on a rota basis, at the cost of relationship-building and caseloads with continuity of care. They believed they were being more efficient, utilising resources in the best way. But, as a result, patient experience is poor, people fall between the cracks, information is lost, decisions are made based on inadequate information, contextual knowledge is lacking and the administrative load is greater, as everything takes longer when the case is unfamiliar. That's a long list. No prizes for guessing where I stand on this issue. Truly integrated teams delivering continuity of care hold the long history, develop trusting working relationships, can respond to subtle early changes in risk, avert a crisis, avoid having to read lots of background information before responding and can complete documentation much more efficiently and meaningfully because they know the case.

In mental health tribunals, colleagues who don't know the full background history flounder when questioned about the need for a compulsory treatment order, as the patient and their lawyer may be stating they will comply and take the medication. They now realise its importance, thus negating the need for the compulsion order. For example, it's helpful to know if there have been episodes of defaulting from medication, when previous orders have been allowed to lapse or the relapse of paranoid illness has resulted in an attempted stabbing. Someone checking the notes may have seen 'no previous convictions' on the patient's record and missed the assault that the patient's partner didn't wish to progress. Our staff would know all about that. One of the social work mental health officers was on the same page as me and came to our team meeting every week, attended joint assessments when we were concerned about a relapse in mental health, collected collateral information from the family and attended mental health tribunals to contribute to making the case for detention. We jointly delivered multi-agency care via the Care Programme Approach (CPA), with the patient, their family, the community psychiatric nurses, addiction service, GP, housing, police and any other agencies involved in the case. This was coordinated, holistic, responsive multi-agency care in action.

The professionalism of our team never ceased to amaze me. In one difficult case, we were working in the dark, with only a vague, unsubstantiated history of mental illness, secure hospital care abroad, offending and deportation to go on. Our patient wasn't willing to enlighten us and the authorities in her home country weren't playing ball. She had no social connections outside our team, so we persevered. We put her on CPA to encourage multi-agency information-sharing, but engagement was minimal. We made some progress when she agreed to meet with me and the psychiatric nurses, but it was superficial. We might at least notice a change in mental state that would signal illness relapse and a need for intervention. She wasn't on a legal order, so there was no compulsion for her to work with us. Then she started to miss appointments and we couldn't locate her at her property. We were encouraged to discharge her but made the decision to keep trying to engage her. In desperation, we considered getting a court order to break into her house, as no one had seen her for weeks. However, staff managed to talk to neighbours, and they said they'd seen her. She appeared to be voting with her feet. We therefore had no grounds to break in to check on her welfare.

Some months later, neighbours noticed flies outside her flat and the council agreed to investigate. Tragically, she had been dead for months. There was literally nothing left of her; all that remained was a mushy pulp on the mattress. It was so, so sad. The Christmas gift from our staff was still sitting on the table, delivered during their last contact with her months before. The council cleaned the flat and we contacted her relatives, who flew in to sort out her affairs. When our staff met with them, they were so grateful to hear about her life in Scotland and the attempts we'd made to try to engage and support her. They wanted to see where she'd been living. Our staff accompanied the family to the flat, only to find that the council had failed to remove the stained mattress. Not surprisingly, this was traumatic for all involved. Despite this, her relatives showed nothing but gratitude. We were criticised by social workers for having kept her on our books, but I still believe it's better to try and fail than to give up on people. Hers was not a good death: alone, in a country where she had no family contact. What does it say about me and my team? We tried to take a person-centred approach. She had no one else and we wanted to keep the door open. We hadn't kept her on our caseload as an active case, as that would have prevented new cases being taken on. We simply felt a commitment to support a vulnerable person. I don't think that aspiration ever left us. Policies and procedures are necessary, but we never underestimated the importance of a large helping of humanity.

Whenever I was invited to explain multidisciplinary teamwork or case management, I usually included a list of potential colleagues: psychiatrists, nurses, psychologists, social workers, criminal justice social workers, occupational therapists, drug and alcohol specialists, police, housing, art therapists, pharmacists and so on. On occasion, we had to spread our net a little further or we'd be contacted by other agencies. If our patients repeatedly sent ranting, psychotic letters to Her Majesty the Queen, we'd receive a polite nudge from the FTAC (Fixated Threat Assessment Centre) to get it sorted. FTAC is the first joint NHS/police unit in the UK. Its purpose is to assess and manage the risks from lone individuals who harass, stalk or threaten public figures. And when we feared that vulnerable, psychotic patients were being groomed online for radicalisation and possible terrorist activities, we were straight on the phone to Prevent for advice from the counterterrorism team. We'd always inform our patients and explain the rationale. Ultimately, we were responsible for treating our patients and reducing the risk of illness-related offending. When the risk level increased, we'd have to consider compulsory admission to hospital for public safety. On more than one occasion, a psychotic patient tried to gain entry to a foreign consulate. They were eventually told that further attempts to cross the threshold may be viewed as a terror attack and they risked being shot. However, this sort of information is difficult for an insightless, psychotic person to comprehend, especially if they believe they've been recruited as an undercover agent.

The prediction of the risk of violence was part of our remit. We were fortunate to have scientifically researched, structured risk assessment tools and clinical forensic psychologists to help us. One of the most well-known tools was the HCR-20. The HCR stands for historical, clinical and risk factors, and there are 20 in total. The predicted level of risk on this tool was only as good as the information, both written and clinical, upon which it was based. My aim was to cover all of these issues in my history-taking so that I could formulate an initial risk assessment and management plan before a more time-consuming full risk assessment was carried out, involving a review of all case files. We always had to manage the patient before the full assessment was available. Therefore clinical judgment was always key in the community. While face-to-face with a patient, you might become aware of a risk factor that had changed since the last visit and would signal a need for immediate action. In some instances, I was at risk and needed to vacate the building immediately. I would, of course, return with reinforcements in uniform. All of our team members had finely tuned virtual risk antennae, developed as a result of lengthy clinical experience and a significant investment in specialist training.

CHAPTER 20

Beanie and Bonzo

They didn't include juggling or plate-spinning modules at university, but that would've been helpful, as alongside the risk assessments, court appearances, ward rounds and prison visits, I was also required to juggle the role of mother to my two *real* babies. I was pregnant with Jill during my higher training and pregnant with Fraser when I started as a consultant. No doubt my employers weren't thrilled about this, due to issues with service cover. However, to be less disruptive to patients and colleagues, I'd decided to take the minimum time off. I'm not sure they realised I was trying to be thoughtful. We named my bump each time: Jill was Beanie and Fraser was Bonzo. Even now, as adults, we sometimes revert to these affectionate terms. How did two children with the same parents turn out to be so different? Jill was a chocolate button blonde cutie and Fraser was a wee cuddly ginger boy. Jill walked at seven-and-a-half months and Fraser couldn't be bothered!

I probably diagnosed Jill's obsessive compulsive disorder earlier than most parents would've done. Thankfully, we were able to access support from my child and adolescent mental health colleagues. It all began with compulsive handwashing and concerns about germs, following some bullying at school and a learning-disabled stranger indecently exposing himself to Jill on holiday. We made the decision to move her from the local primary school at the age of eight to a small private school near my workplace. I became a taxi mum for the next 13 years. We were open about the OCD in the hope that they could support her to deal with it. If we'd waited to move her until the first year at high school, she would've been two years behind in French and German. It was a great success, but with Fraser due to start school the following year, we found ourselves having to fund two private school educations, which was not part of our financial plan. I'm not sure we even had a plan. It's the incidentals that you don't account for: the awful summer dresses (were material belts and puffed sleeves ever in fashion?), the hockey trip to Canada, skiing lessons, the ski trip to Andorra, keyboard lessons, swimming club, swimming galas, judo, fencing, hockey, drums, cello, French horn, drama lessons, debating club and so on. The most enduring extra-curricular activities were Jill's swimming and Fraser's singing lessons from Mr H., who'd performed with Scottish Opera. He attended religiously every week from age seven to 19, attended the Royal Conservatoire for Scotland's Saturday drama school for seven years, and regularly performed with Youth Music Theatre Scotland in Fife. Then there was the Duke of Edinburgh Award and the Young Enterprise Company Programme. Richard and I sacrificed 20 years of our social lives to drive around the country for musical theatre shows, ski races and swimming galas, but emerged as very proud parents.

Jill is the sociable people-person who's tone deaf and wouldn't be seen dead on a stage. Fraser is more private, preferring a close-knit group of like-minded musical theatre friends, but feels comfortable addressing large audiences at conferences, taking part in debating competitions and donning a costume to perform to theatres full of people, entertaining them with his rich baritone voice and acting skills. Their responsible natures were recognised early on, with Jill being chosen as head girl, followed five years later by Fraser as deputy head boy. In his final yearbook, Fraser's friends said he was the one most likely to become prime minister. He can be a confident and authoritative orator and has phenomenal organisational skills. I've always said that he came out of the womb wearing a suit. However, despite his clear articulation on stage, Fraser's communication with his parents could be assessed as 'could do better'. One summer as a teenager, he was an arts practitioner on a junior production of *Bugsy Malone*. He was asked to assist with a small walk-on part during which he would be shot by gangsters with a splurge gun that fired silly string from canisters. Fraser, being very tall, was too big for the junior production, so they decided that he would walk in front of the front row of the audience, several feet below the stage. Essentially his head and upper torso were at stage level, so his top half would be attacked with the silly string from the stage.

We were relaxing at home when a text arrived from Fraser: 'Chemical burns to face. In A&E in Kirkcaldy.' All rational thought abandoned me. I had visions of my beautiful teenage boy with his face melting off like molten wax. We were an hour's drive away. It was the longest journey. When we arrived, Fraser was with the doctor. We found out that the gun had misfired and, instead of silly string, chemicals had hit his face and eyes and irritated them. He'd gone a bit red, but thankfully there were no third-degree chemical burns. For Fraser, the show must go on, so he was anxious to return for the evening performance. His friends had received a similar text and Chinese whispers had him scarred for life. As a result, before the audience were allowed in for the evening show, I was met with a sea of anxious faces, queuing up in sympathy to give their best wishes. There was only one occasion when I was happy to see his face scarred, and that was when he wore a prosthetic mask to play the role of the Phantom in *Phantom of the Opera*. It was absolutely fantastic. He even had a little tuft of ginger hair in his prosthesis to make it lifelike. We were obviously biased, but seeing him play that role with his best friend Katherine playing Christine was one of my proudest moments.

His desire for the show to go on became a bit of a theme. Not long after he'd passed his driving test, he was driving on the motorway to rehearsals for yet another show in Fife, a regular occurrence for many years. I was in my outpatient clinic when I had an early morning interruption.

'Dr Morrison, can you please call your husband? It's an emergency.'

I quickly concluded the appointment and made the call, terrified at the prospect of bad news and assuming the worst. Richard told me, 'Fraser's been in a motorway accident. He's written off his car. He swerved to avoid the wheel arch of an HGV that was sitting in the middle of the road and lost control of the car. I think he over-steered.' Most young drivers who had written off their car, nearly ploughed over the side of a bridge and ended up facing oncoming traffic on the motorway would be in shock, but not Fraser: 'Can you drive me to rehearsals in Kirkcaldy please? I don't want to be late.'

In 2017, Fraser stood in the local council elections as an independent candidate, roping us into doing leaflet drops to 7,000 houses. Then he persuaded me to do some door-to-door canvassing. It was an educational experience. Who knew there were such things as aggressive letterboxes? These were the ones that had a double set of bristles attached. They tried to prevent you from posting anything through them and ripped your hands to shreds on the way back out. Despite this, I quite enjoyed canvassing, and when I told friends and colleagues about my exploits, they seemed quite jealous. One evening, I rang a doorbell and stood on the path, awaiting a response. I heard two dogs barking and saw some movement behind the opaque glass panel of the door, but no one answered. I decided to lean forward and post the leaflet through yet another aggressive letterbox. I was standing two steps down when the door suddenly opened to reveal a naked, tattooed young man wearing a small white towel that barely covered his groin, which was at my eye level.

I addressed his groin: 'Are you thinking of voting in the local election?'

'I was just about to get into the bath.'

Despite my previous experience in dealing with patients, I was too embarrassed to say much at all.

Even though Fraser wasn't elected, he received plenty of first votes and positive feedback. He continues to do a lot of charity work, organising musical theatre concerts with his friends. For his 21st birthday, he organised a fundraising concert for the children's hospital and performed with his musical theatre pals in front of an invited audience of 150 or so friends and family. They raised more than £1,600. He'd spent time there as a young boy, visiting A&E, outpatients and day surgery with an assortment of ailments including perforated eardrums, broken arms, suspected meningitis, difficulty breathing, tonsillitis and hearing impairment, and wanted to give something back. He also managed to deliver a solo performance at the Women's Guild with a temperature of 98 degrees, only to be admitted to hospital with pneumonia a few hours later.

Jill's access to healthcare has been more enduring. Since developing OCD, she has had two courses of CBT (cognitive behavioural therapy) and various courses of medication, and continues to deal with residual symptoms on a day-to-day basis. She has to cope with intrusive thoughts and self-doubt, and feels compelled to report her 'stupid thoughts' to me on a daily basis. She also feels compelled to list her activities: 'I've been making cupcakes, doing the dishes, tidying the flat; I think I'll have pizza for tea; I think I upset someone, I didn't mean to...' These calls almost always conclude with a 'confession', which is her way of dumping her intrusive thoughts. She feels less anxious about them for a while, but is more likely to repeat the behaviour, so my role is to discourage her. If interrupted, she's likely to repeat the detailed list. It's to her credit that she's gone on to achieve so much. It's hard to be the understanding psychiatrist when you're the emotionally involved mum, but I do my best. Jill is generous to a fault and would go out of her way to help anyone. She's kind, caring and totally honest. She will never lie to you, as she feels compelled to tell the truth. People value her honesty, but sometimes it can be brutal.

When Jill was 24, she applied to the prison service to train as an officer. After graduating as the top academic recruit in her cohort, she was posted to Cornton Vale. She subsequently transferred to HMPYOI Polmont, the national male young offenders' prison. While there, she had an unfortunate experience. On opening one of the door hatches to perform a check at the end of her nightshift, she found an 18-year-old man hanging there and had to cut him down. We found ourselves sitting at the suicide review together, having to declare a conflict of interest. I believe a little bit of my view of the world has rubbed off on Jill. She also has a passion for the rehabilitation of offenders. She's interested in their stories, is respectful, tries to be non-judgemental and wants to support them to turn the corner and achieve success post liberation. She and others like her will be the ones who shape the culture and attitude in the prisons of the future.

CHAPTER 21

A Life Sentence

HMP Cornton Vale is located in the upmarket suburb of Bridge of Allan on the outskirts of Stirling, where huge houses overlook the Wallace Monument and Stirling Castle. Even the bars on the prison windows are more in keeping with the location. Painted white, they have vertical spars interspersed with rounded square rings of metal, so they look a bit like fancy wrought iron gates rather than bars. These had clearly been designed with positive intent, but the reality was that every cell featured horizontal metal ligature points that you could use to hang yourself with a bedsheet or laces. The Scottish Centre for Crime and Justice Research reported that the prison suicide rate for 2015–2018 was 125 per 100,000, which is substantially higher than in England and Wales, and around ten times the rate for the general population of Scotland. There was a spate of suicides at Cornton Vale that hit the media while I was a trainee on a six-month placement. I remember sitting around the large, shiny boardroom table in the governor's management suite, drinking tea from the posh china served by one of the trusted prisoners. A meeting had been convened to discuss the way forward. Suggestions from the psychiatrists included removing the ornate wrought ironwork. We'd also be getting a demo of new designs for anti-ligature, anti-suicide gear. This is when I encountered what I refer to as the Dalek suit. It wasn't exactly practical. It was so stiff and long that I don't think anyone would've been able to sit down in it. We opted for a shorts and T-shirt combo in thick, blue, quilted fabric that had no zips or ties and could be adjusted to fit with Velcro fasteners. The fabric was difficult to rip and there were no sleeves or legs that could be used as ligatures. High-risk prisoners would find themselves barefoot, in the shorts and T-shirt suit, with a rubberised mattress on the floor. The 'sui cells' were redesigned to take account of observation requirements and removal of any possible ligature points such as door handles and light fittings. Bathrooms required specially designed showers without shower heads, again to reduce ligature points.

Little did I know at the time, but Cornton Vale would go on to play a special role in my life. I'm not sure why, but I'd always found violent, paranoid men easier to deal with, even in the hospital wards. Perhaps the reason for this gradually emerged from having increasing clinical contact with female offenders. Many of them had been victims of complex trauma and emotional, physical and sexual abuse. They experienced post-traumatic stress-related nightmares in custody, particularly when they were coming off illicit drugs and alcohol (their coping strategies in the community) and their sleep pattern was disrupted. They often had emergent emotionally unstable personality disorders and a high incidence of impulsive, deliberate self-harm. My afternoon clinic list could have up to eight new referrals, all with complex trauma and post-traumatic stress disorder, and at least three or four would've attempted self-harm or tied a ligature round their neck that week. Short of laying on of hands, it wasn't clear what I was supposed to do. It was emotionally draining work, so I developed a psychological coping strategy. After seeing each patient, trying to empathise with them, offer support and put a risk management plan in place, I needed to clear my head, or I wouldn't be able to be emotionally present for the next one. I guess it was a form of dissociation. I cut off my emotions and compartmentalised them in order to deal with the next onslaught.

I worked at Cornton Vale three times during my higher training, and found myself working there again as a consultant, this time as the regular prison psychiatrist, running two clinics per week. In total, I was the prison psychiatrist on and off for 18 years, which is more than a life sentence. But at least I got to go home at night.

In the course of my work, I was invited to join a national working party that was tasked with reviewing the management of deliberate self-harm. There were representatives from psychology, psychiatry, prison, high-secure care and the Scottish government. I listened to the expert advice of esteemed colleagues regarding the causes of self-harm and the current advice regarding management options. There was a suggestion that staff should give minimal input to patients/prisoners after an incident in order to avoid rewarding the behaviour with staff attention and risk repetition of the behaviour. The focus of the discussion appeared to be on non-life-threatening, superficial self-harm. I suddenly found myself saying 'Have any of you actually worked at Cornton Vale?'

My patients often lacked the emotional vocabulary to express their feelings, finding it easier to tolerate self-inflicted physical pain than emotional distress, for which they lacked adequate coping strategies. Their extreme self-harming behaviour had often resulted in rejection by local psychiatric services, where they had been labelled as 'personality disordered', which seemed to be a ticket out of services. We were the default national service when things went wrong. If the person threatening to jump from a bridge on Saturday night had been labelled as personality disordered, local services would tell the police that inpatient care wouldn't help. The police would then charge them with breach of the peace and hold them in the cells over the weekend to keep them safe. The next day the sheriff would remand them to prison, just to make sure they weren't released from court only to try again.

Many of these women had resorted to drugs to blank out abuse-related nightmares and would need a methadone detox in custody. Some were so desperate for a fix that they regurgitated the methadone and sold their 'methadone spit' to other prisoners as a swap for diazepam. It was a currency within the prison. If they knew a custodial sentence was likely, they would sometimes bring in razor blades hidden in their vagina. Others smuggled illicit drugs in this way. If fellow inmates suspected they were hiding drugs, they might attack them in the shower, pin them to the ground and manually evacuate them, which was tantamount to rape. I was likely to meet the victim of the assault in my clinic. Homemade ligatures were not uncommon, with Code BLUE calls for respiratory arrest a regular occurrence. Code RED was used when there was significant blood loss. There were also more unusual incidents, such as trying to cut off nipples and throwing bleach in their own eyes. You couldn't predict what extreme behaviour they would try next. It was such a sad reflection on their lives. They were predictably unpredictable and impulsive.

Back in the psychiatric hospital ward, we had incidents involving patients burning their flesh with an iron and then putting dirt in the wound, setting fire to their clothes and swallowing batteries from the radio. Again, I would hear terms like 'manipulative and attention-seeking'. I hated that. They just didn't have the skills to communicate their distress or cope with it in a more appropriate way. Some patients in the community threatened the police with a gun, in the hope that the police would shoot them. You'd need to be pretty desperate to do that. There were no quick fixes. The women who ended up with the longer sentences in custody did the best. There was time for them to get off the dysfunctional merry-go-round.

CHAPTER 22

Get an Officer!

The BBC made a documentary about Cornton Vale. It was called *Girls Behind Bars*, and I appeared briefly in one episode. It wasn't my finest hour, and to make it worse I was six stones overweight. The film crew featured several prisoners and planned to follow them post-liberation. The prison staff informed me that there was an urgent need for me to see one of the featured prisoners, who had recently made a suicide attempt. She was due for liberation, and they didn't want the BBC to follow her out in case she killed herself. Considerable pressure was exerted on me to arrange a pris-on-to-hospital transfer. Fortunately, after a long debate with a colleague in Aberdeen, I negotiated the transfer, somewhat against my better judgement. I could justify it because she did constitute a risk to herself, but I wasn't convinced that inpatient care was going to be therapeutic for someone with substance misuse and emotionally unstable personality disorder. The plan was to inform her at the case conference, which she'd agreed could be filmed. I was less keen. Needless to say, she didn't take it well. In the episode, they cut to her cell. It showed her being extremely angry and trying to run at the cell door to come and get me, screaming 'F***ing boot.' Being called a f***ing boot on national TV was not my crowning glory. It felt as if everyone who had ever known me saw that programme: my husband's barber, a boy from school (whom I hadn't seen for 30 years), a stranger in the waiting room at the prison, everyone at work, my kids' school friends, they'd all watched it.

Because Cornton Vale has featured throughout my career, it's therefore an integral part of it. I took many trainee psychiatrists and medical students to the prison clinic over the years, but often failed to realise the impact that some of the prisoners and their stories had on them. Having somehow developed a coping strategy for dealing with the multiple stories of complex trauma, I was able to see several prisoners with heart-wrenching stories back-to-back. It wasn't as easy for my colleagues. On one occasion, the only interview space available was the health centre treatment room used by visiting obstetricians and gynaecologists. It had a couch, stirrups, shiny trays and canisters containing metal instruments, which were useful if you wanted to do a vaginal examination. Thankfully that was not part of my normal psychiatric practice. I sat at the desk beside the distraught prisoner who'd been convicted of a brutal murder and was now experiencing nightmares and flashbacks of the crime. Two medical students were sitting behind me, next to the trolley and instruments. Suddenly and quite unexpectedly the prisoner got up, lunged past me and between the medical students, grabbed the long-handled metal forceps and tried to stab herself in the chest. I leapt up, bear-hugged her from behind, fixing her upper arms to the side of her body to prevent her having any leverage to use the forceps as a weapon.

'Get an officer!'

The students, mouths open, didn't move. They were in total shock and, as far as I was concerned, they were useless. I didn't tell them that, obviously. It wasn't very understanding of me, but the situation was stressful, and I could've done with some help. The situation resolved itself when I shouted, and officers intervened.

Once back in compassionate psychiatrist mode, I held a debrief and apologised to the medical students for their distressing experience. But for me, it was just another day at the office.

I met many interesting people during my time at Cornton Vale. A person's upbringing doesn't excuse their future behaviour or the need for punishment, but it can set them on a bumpy path. What drives someone to abduct a person and hold them hostage, murder a pregnant woman, stab their neighbour, embezzle company funds, or groom children for a paedophile ring? I strongly believe that prisoners who receive a three-year sentence or more do the best. They're given a drug-free opportunity for reparenting by staff, they can learn emotional coping strategies and develop trust. There's an incentive to engage in prosocial behaviour, as they'll be rewarded with a better quality of life in custody. I thought the solution would be to have a system that worked in the same way as points on your driving licence. You'd receive points for each minor crime committed, and when you reached a specified threshold, you'd be given three or more years in custody. It would save the money that's currently being spent on ineffective short-term sentences and act as a true deterrent. It would also give offenders an opportunity for true learning and long-term behavioural change. So, that's sentencing reform sorted!

My next reform project was trying to influence the remit of the forensic community mental health service. I wanted to push boundaries, but not everyone agreed. They say prevention is better than cure; I've always thought that made sense, but in most forensic services one of the entry criteria is to have committed an illness-driven crime, i.e. be a mentally disordered offender. That means the horse needs to have bolted. By that point, there will already be a victim and the patient will be facing a lengthy inpatient stay in a secure hospital setting. When I set up the community forensic service, I thought we should also see people who had the potential to become forensic patients. For example, a patient may develop a psychotic illness and be found to have a stockpile of weapons under their bed. Their symptoms may include command auditory hallucinations instructing them to attack prostitutes, in the context of delusional beliefs that they're the chosen one and have to rid the world of sexual depravity. Following admission and treatment in hospital, I'd argue that they'd benefit from the more intense follow-up that's offered by a forensic service to monitor for early signs of illness relapse and for public protection. Technically, they're not a mentally disordered offender – at least, not yet. I had many heated debates with colleagues about this. But, as lead clinician, in cases where I felt strongly that prevention was better than a crime, I made the decision to sneak a few cases onto my caseload. When someone was worried that they were going to rape a stranger, there was no other appropriate service willing to assess them or work with them because they didn't fit anyone's service criteria. In my view, ruling out treatable mental illness and generating a risk management plan were part of that prevention agenda. My peers considered it to be controversial, but it didn't stop me from seeking an opinion from a clinical forensic psychologist and another forensic psychiatrist and coming up with a plan. In the prison, I was occasionally asked to see a high-profile prisoner, not because of acute concern about their mental health or behaviour, but to offer emotional support as a preventative measure. For example, there was a prisoner involved in a high-profile abduction and torture case who was subjected to a punishment regime decided by their peers. Threats of scarring, secondary to boiling sugar water being thrown at them, would be detrimental to anyone's mental health.

Staff at HMYOI Polmont were always concerned when they had a young person in custody or a case was receiving excessive media attention. My role as the prison psychiatrist was to support the mental health of those inmates within the institution; I had no role within the legal process. One particular young man had no requirement to be assessed by me or to cooperate. Although he came to my clinic, he chose not to engage. I had to respect that. A therapeutic relationship takes two people, so what I could offer was minimal. However, not for the first time in my career, I wondered how much the jury might be influenced when confronted, as I was, with someone who came across as emotionally unperturbed and detached. Was this a feature of their personality or a deliberate attempt not to engage, to avoid incriminating themselves? I'll never know. I still worry that this young man was unsupported in dealing with the emotional impact of the death of his girlfriend, finding her mutilated body, being accused of her murder, being taken into custody and facing a murder trial under intense media scrutiny. His lack of engagement may have been because he was advised not to discuss it with anyone. I can't deny that, at a human-interest level, I would love to have understood more about what had happened, but that was not my role. The newspaper accounts relating to other high-profile cases I'd been involved with never seemed to reflect the nuances of the case and tended to go for the sensationalist headline, which often bore little resemblance to the person sitting in front of me in my clinic. The young man continued to protest his innocence after conviction. Perhaps we'll never know the true story. But what I do know is that if you don't extend a helping hand, some people who need it may come to harm.

As my consultant role changed and I took on additional management responsibilities as associate medical director for mental health services, I eventually said my farewell to Cornton Vale. However, I was still managing the prison psychiatrists. Later, during a year-long stint as general manager (a further additional role on top of the day job), I found myself managing three national prison healthcare teams. Cornton Vale was one of them. After my general management spell, I thought I'd been liberated again, but not for long because I had to review all the suicides in Forth Valley. This time it was the suicide of a female prisoner. I felt a bit like a recalled prisoner. I escaped again, but not for the last time.

CHAPTER 23

The Kilted Suitor

It was the day before Christmas Eve. In the tinsel-adorned waiting room of the GP surgery, puddles of gritty, melting snow formed on the floor around the boots of the scarved, coughing patients. An icy draught announced each new arrival. I'd squeezed in an extra forensic outpatient clinic before the holiday break, hoping to review any patients the team were concerned about, if they could be bothered or organised enough to turn up. We'd just received a referral for a man recently discharged from the intensive psychiatric care unit, who'd been under the care of my forensic consultant colleague but would be transferring to my care. The service standard was to review patients within one week of discharge as this is often a high-risk period, so he'd been added to the list for a pre-Christmas appointment. I certainly wasn't expecting my new patient to be in full Highland dress! Kilts were not required attire for attending a doctor's appointment in Scotland.

'Hi, I'm Dr Morrison. Pleased to meet you. I'm so sorry for sending an appointment so close to Christmas. You should have called, and we could have rescheduled. Have you come straight from a wedding?'

'No,' he replied, looking bemused.

There was a pregnant pause as I tried to work out what was going on.

'I just dressed to impress you.'

'Oh... very smart.'

I wasn't sure how to respond, simply noting it as a bit odd. As we continued, he seemed very chatty and overfamiliar, with a hint of paranoia. The warning signs were there, as he'd recently been discharged from hospital. I didn't have a baseline to judge his presentation against. Was this resolving illness or early relapse?

'I have a letter from the doctor telling me what's been happening recently. Would you like to tell me from your perspective?'

'She had lovely legs. I dream about her in a bikini, on a beach in Bermuda. I'd like to ask her out to lunch.'

Well, that was a bit of sexual disinhibition right there. It wasn't the typical reaction a doctor gets when she detains you under the Mental Health Act, locks you up in hospital and compels you to take antipsychotic medication. He didn't appear to represent an acute risk to himself or others, but would need to be closely monitored. Our wonderful nursing team came to the rescue in these circumstances, visiting patients at home multiple times per week if necessary. They would establish a rapport and monitor symptoms along with the fluctuating risk level. Many of the patients managed by our team were on our caseload for several years and we'd begin to notice subtle changes in presentation that heralded potential illness relapse. These changes were not always as obvious or unusual as patients who were anxious about helicopters full of MI6 spies, slept under the bed with a radio to monitor snipers in fighter planes or believed that people had entered their house overnight to use their boots and replaced them by morning in a different location. Sometimes it was simply a reduction in eye contact, a preoccupation with a particular person, or a slightly paranoid interpretation of events, attributing more meaning to someone's behaviour than would be perceived as normal. A patient's previous history of psychotically driven offending meant that any increased risk of altercations had to be monitored and managed with extra nurse visits, an urgent psychiatric outpatient review, a home visit, a change in medication or whatever their risk management plan suggested. We used to joke about other psychiatric teams who'd refer patients to our team because they were 'too risky' for their team. I'd put up a slide during lectures picturing a suit of armour and a tank, a joke about our team and standard-issue nurse uniforms and lease vehicles to conduct home visits. For the avoidance of doubt, there were no special uniforms or armoured vehicles. The staff were, however, brave, highly skilled practitioners with a huge amount of integrity and compassion, who were experts in interpersonal communication as well as risk assessment and management.

If it has been established that a patient may present a potential risk to the public when they experience a relapse of illness and there are concerns regarding non-compliance with medication or monitoring, some patients remain on Mental Health Act orders in the community. This compels them to take medication and remain in contact with services. In such cases, at regular intervals, the psychiatrist, mental health social worker and community nurse would attend an independent mental health tribunal, which includes a panel comprised of a lawyer, psychiatrist and a layperson with no links to the health board. We'd submit paperwork in advance, which stated the grounds for the order to be kept in place. Copies would also be shared with the patient in advance, allowing them time to seek independent legal representation and, if they disagreed, an independent psychiatric opinion.

So how do psychiatrists decide whether or not someone has a mental illness? The mental state examination is the psychiatrist's equivalent of the GP's physical examination. It's where psychiatrists elicit the symptom patterns that help us come up with the diagnosis. Anyone can read about the list of symptoms and the definition of psychotic symptoms, but you have to encounter them for real to understand their essence. We encouraged junior staff to write verbatim accounts of an abnormal mental state when taking a history, as it can be interpreted later. It's a bit like being a detective, looking for all the clues to solve the case. If you want to play armchair psychiatrist, there's a lot to cover. On most occasions, the forensic team would be sitting on a grubby chair in someone's living room, in a police cell, on low NHS 'comfy' chairs (too low to get out of in a hurry, if an angry man decided to bop you), or standing with a foot in the door because our patient had refused entry. The symptoms to be examined included: appearance, behaviour, engagement, rapport, eye contact, facial expression, body language, abnormal movement or posture, speech (rate, quality, tone, volume, fluency and rhythm), mood, thoughts (form, content, delusions, possession, speed, flow, coherence), perception (hallucinations, pseudo-hallucinations, illusions, depersonalisation, derealisation), cognition, insight, judgement and so on.

Here's a myth-buster for you: not all Scottish men wear kilts and eat haggis, and not all psychiatrists get you to lie down on a couch to ask about your granny! I've never used a couch. Sometimes my patients locked themselves in a bedroom and ranted at me to leave or banged their head on a brick wall while rapping loudly with a tirade of expletives. In severe mental illness, patients may not understand that they have a mental illness, believing their experiences to be real. For example, they may hear voices outside their head making derogatory comments about them and believe they're being monitored and persecuted by the government, so they barricade themselves in the house. If they think poisonous gas is being fed into their house, they may tape round the windows and block the letterbox and toilet. Patients who don't recognise they're unwell are said to lack insight. The same symptoms occur in more than one disorder. It's the recognisable combination or pattern of symptoms and behaviours that will lead to a diagnosis, just as in physical medicine. Here are some examples:

Question: 'You told the nurse you're the King of Scotland, is that right?'

This is a false belief that's an example of a grandiose delusion. It's important to check, as the grandiose claims may sometimes be real or culturally acceptable. As we have a queen in the UK, I felt I was on safe ground with this one.

Answer: 'I don't like poached stickleback fish!'

This response to the question about being the King of Scotland made no sense. Clearly there's no obvious link between the question and the answer. The patient's thought processes were affected by his schizophrenic illness. The interaction demonstrated thought disorder.

Delusions are idiosyncratic, false beliefs maintained by the individual despite being contradicted by reality or rational argument. For example: 'The masons have injected the genes for the human race into my scalp. The government is trying to get them to create clones. I can't wash my hair, or I might lose them.' This is a paranoid delusional system. The patient may not have washed their hair for nine months (the behaviour is consistent with the delusions, demonstrating lack of insight). While teaching, I used to give a silly example, but one that people would understand. If someone had the delusional belief that they were a Mars Bar, they'd refuse to sleep next to the radiator in the ward in case they were murdered (melted) during the night. When someone has a fixed, delusional belief about something, their behaviour is consistent with that.

In medical school, we were taught to recognise patterns of symptoms. If someone presents to the GP with a rapid three-stone weight loss, a cough, bloody spit and smokes 60 cigarettes per day, the GP doesn't say 'Let me examine your genitals'. Until proven otherwise, they're probably thinking of lung cancer, and will suggest appropriate tests such as a chest X-ray and sputum sample. Psychiatrists are medical doctors, so we look for similar symptom patterns. The most striking difference is that there often isn't much to find on physical examination, in blood tests or scans, although they're sometimes needed to exclude a physical cause for the symptoms. Establishing a rapport, history-taking and observation become key. When I was trying to explain the pattern of symptoms to look out for in bipolar disorder (manic depression), I had to outline the differences between manic/hypomanic and depressed states. I'd invite my trainee to imagine the Duracell bunny from the TV adverts. Depression is a bit like when the batteries in the bunny run low: low energy, slow speech, eyes down, poor eye contact, shoulders down, low mood, paucity of movement, exhausted, poor self-care, negative thoughts, nihilistic delusions, poor appetite, weight loss, poor concentration, memory impairment, lack of libido and sometimes suicidal thoughts. On the other hand, mania/hypomania is like doubling the number of batteries inside the bunny: overactivity, racing thoughts, loud and pressured speech, elevated mood, flight of ideas, disinhibited behaviour, irritability, insomnia (due to too much energy), multitasking, distractibility, overspending, promiscuity and grandiosity. Until confronted by someone who's delusional, thought disordered, has an altered mood or is hallucinating, it's unlikely that you'll truly understand it.

Compared to other specialties, the complex problem with psychiatry is the lack of test results to clinch the diagnosis. We don't culture bacteria or find a shadow on an X-ray. Instead, we may be presented with someone who's mute and making no eye contact, a man in full Highland dress who has a crush on the doctor who detained him or someone talking to an invisible fish finger. We need to be skilled observers of human behaviour and pick up on subtle changes in thought content or form. That's what made the on-call consultant role so stressful.

Relying on the observational skills of a junior doctor who may only have been doing psychiatry for two weeks meant that giving advice in the middle of the night was not for the faint-hearted.

CHAPTER 24

Damn Cats

We used to have appointments with some of our patients in an old sandstone building on the outskirts of the most deprived part of town known for its community of drug users and Saturday night brawls. The psychiatric day hospital was far from ideal, but it was in an accessible community location, and we hoped that would improve attendance rates. However, there was a downside to borrowing rooms in another team's building, as I was sometimes allocated the rooms that no one else wanted. They were down a long, dark corridor, through a door and beyond screaming distance if I had an emergency. Someone had tried to make it less clinical by installing soft seating. The intent was positive, but the reality was dangerous. They were low in height, so my knees ended up above hip height, making it difficult to stand up. I certainly wouldn't be lunging towards the door in a hurry. The alternative was the desk chair, but it was so narrow that my pear-shaped bottom wouldn't fit. If I'd tried to stand up quickly, it would've come with me and I'd have been sprouting wood and metal plumage, on wheels, from my behind. And so I took my chances on the stained, scratchy weave of the low, soft seating. People entering the building had to queue at the glass-fronted reception window to state their name and which professional they were there to see. I joined the queue, as I was also a visitor. The wait in reception was fascinating. I'd play 'guess the diagnosis' in my head, trying to work out what was going on by body language alone. If I was waiting to see a new patient, I'd try to guess who was there to see me. There was a professional-looking woman, smartly dressed, eyes down and wringing her hands... anxiety? An older, dishevelled man was muttering distractedly to himself in the corner... schizophrenia? A young woman in bright lipstick and garish clothes was talking loudly to anyone who'd listen, sharing more information than was appropriate... hypomania? The door opened and a young man in a tracksuit entered, hoodie up, which was always a bad sign. I didn't think he'd turn up, as he'd missed his previous appointment.

'I'm here tae see Mrs Morrison. She'd better no' be late, cos I've tae see ma probation officer at hauf three. If she's no' here, I'm f***ing oot a here!'

'Hi, I'm Dr Morrison. Once we find out which room we're in, I'll take you straight through.'

We sat opposite each other... waiting. Eyes down, he scanned from side to side, his left knee bobbing up and down frantically in an agitated 'I could explode at any moment' fashion. I needed 90 minutes for my court assessment, but the clock was already ticking on the 30 minutes he'd scheduled in his head. If he didn't complete the assessment, he risked remand to prison for reports. 'He's not going to like that,' I thought. 'I hope I don't get the interview room down the back corridor...'

When I informed him that my court assessment was likely to last for an hour and a half, he went into full rant mode, swearing loudly, his threatening glare adding to the already highly charged atmosphere. He seemed to think it was all my fault, conveniently overlooking his failure to attend the previous appointment.

'Do you have your probation officer's telephone number? Let me give them a call to explain and we'll see what we can sort out.'

As usual, the result of the phone call would depend on the personality of the criminal justice social worker and how flexible they were willing to be. I was in the room down the back corridor, so I was crossing my fingers for a pal at the end of the phone. It was a relief to discover that I knew them. We negotiated an alternative appointment.

It was in the same day hospital that I met another interesting man. As the interview progressed, I got to his sexual history...

'So, tell me, did you get sexual education at school? Are you more interested in men or women? What do you understand by the word privacy in relation to sex? Do you know what consent means? Do you know what date rape means? Are you aware of the legal age of consent? It's normal to masturbate – what do you use to get aroused? Do you get aroused by pornography, children, animals, bondage, S&M, force, violence, fires, homo-sexuality? Has anyone ever been inappropriate to you in a sexual way? I've asked you lots of detailed questions, but there may be one very specific thing that gets you aroused that I've not asked about. You're not going to say anything that I haven't heard before.'

'Yes, there is,' he replied, pausing before continuing in a deep, menacing voice, which I was sure he'd deliberately lowered a few octaves, 'I'd tie him to a tree, slit him from his breastbone to his pubic bone, take his intestines out, lay them on the table, cut off his head, put it in his stomach, sew him back up and set fire to him.'

Well, that's not what I was expecting... my inner swan was back. Trying not to look rattled, I continued.

'Have you ever acted on that fantasy?'

'No, the bastard died before I could do it...'

In the fullness of time, it turned out that he wasn't my only outpatient to have decapitation fantasies. When confronted with any startling or concerning response, it was always important to go on a deep dive to establish the trigger to the fantasy. There was almost certainly a traumatic story to be unearthed, as the venom was often real and the victim very specific. If a history involved childhood abuse of some sort, building trust and respect would be key to our therapeutic relationship. If anger management issues were mentioned in the referral letter and we were going to deal with any unresolved emotion, we needed to be mindful of our own personal safety and that of our colleagues. In an attempt at person-centred care, with a patient's consent, we'd sometimes share the pertinent parts of their history within the multi-agency risk management plan. There was a special section for police colleagues, which meant we could offer guidance about how to interact with our patients. For example: 'If you're going to arrest this woman, ask her to get into the police car and she'll come quietly. If you lay hands on her, it will trigger traumatic memories and she's likely to respond violently.' There were often no further police assault charges after that. Other changes we noted included violent, psychotic males with trauma histories eventually allowing a male nurse to enter their home to administer their antipsychotic medication, which involved a male nurse giving an injection in their buttock. What a huge step forward in terms of trust.

A background history of complex trauma was a recurrent theme for many patients. Unless there was a history of sexual offending or sexual abuse, I didn't routinely take a sexual history. Not surprisingly, violent, paranoid men found it quite intrusive. During another assessment, one patient disclosed a history of pinning cats to trees and setting fire to them. Fire-raising is sometimes linked to deviant sexual arousal, so I made the decision to take his sexual history. As I was doing this, I became distracted.

'What happened to your anorak?' I enquired, having noticed singe marks.

'Damn cats!'

Having to tell patients that you need to breach their confidentiality when you learn that a crime has been committed often threatens the therapeutic relationship. However, in reality, if you explain the duty of a doctor in terms of public safety and protection (with a caveat that you want to help them reduce the risk of future offending, and you can't do that if they keep offending and getting locked up), they usually understand. This patient opted to remain engaged with me. I think the key is to remain respectful and non-judgemental, explain the rationale for reporting an offence, include them where possible, and reiterate the desire to support them to reduce the risk of future offending. Treating people as adults, on an adult-to-adult basis, rather than having them perceive the doctor as the critical, controlling parent/authority figure and feeling victimised as a result, means the therapeutic relationship is already beginning to evolve on a healthier basis. They knew that I was on their side, but there were boundaries, and if they crossed them there would be a consistent consequence. The consequence was not a discharge from services, which may have been their previous experience. They may not have had an authority figure or role model who'd been supportive before. Trust takes a long time to build, especially if it has been abused by others.

CHAPTER 25

The Perils of Werther's Originals

Back in my days as a junior psychiatrist, I recall having to choose my words carefully when dealing with a rather mysterious, socially awkward man. He seemed quite paranoid, but otherwise showed little emotion and just stared at me, giving monosyllabic answers. He brought a heavy carrier bag with him to every appointment, and I started to fantasise about its contents. In this particular month, in my mind it was an axe. But, just before Christmas, there was a change to his routine. I was about to end the appointment when his hand delved deep into the bag. He'd never done that before. Everything went into slow motion as I watched intently for his hand to re-emerge with... a large jar of sweeties.

'I made some butterscotch sweeties for you, doctor.'

My paranoia went into overdrive. I started to think he'd poisoned them. When he'd gone, I tested one out on a colleague. Thankfully, they survived! I became the sweetie doctor again as a consultant, but this time I wasn't receiving them or giving them out to my patients. In medicine, we constantly tell people what's detrimental to their health and wellbeing, so perhaps I should warn you about the perils of Werther's Originals. We were sitting in a large group therapy room in a circle of comfy chairs, with a small coffee table in the centre. I asked the student nurse if she'd heard of CPA. She shook her head. 'Let me explain,' I began. 'Don't sit in a meeting and not ask questions. Asking questions is the only way to learn. In complex cases, we use the Care Programme Approach, or CPA, to manage multi-disciplinary, multi-agency, holistic care. The services involved in the care plan meet face-to-face with the user and carer as a group, twice per year, to agree the new care plan, and it's minuted. Essentially, it's good practice written down.'

The patient joined us when everyone was in the room. He was a tall young man who'd been misusing illicit drugs as a form of self-medication for his bipolar disorder. He was quite a character, often randomly announcing that he liked my earrings, popping tablets during appointments, putting his feet up on the radiator, slugging a pint of milk or, if he happened to see me there, giving me a hug in the middle of the shopping centre. To keep us on our toes when we went on home visits, he kept a baseball bat by the front door. All I can say is that he'd never played baseball in his life. His care team included me, his forensic community mental health nurse, the student nurse and staff from the addiction team, social work and housing. The main man himself seemed keen to get started.

'Dr Morrison, I've kicked my heroin addiction.'

'That's great, really well done.'

'But I'm addicted to something else now...'

A brief pause for dramatic effect.

'Werther's Originals.'

He proceeded to produce a bag of the butterscotch sweeties from his pocket. After a collective giggle, we continued with the meeting while he smiled, sucked and chewed his way through the whole bag. Halfway through the meeting, he began to make odd gurgling sounds, started drooling and turned purple. He was clearly choking. And I thought heroin was dangerous... My colleagues looked on but failed to intervene. I was going to have to step in. Despite being medically trained, my last physical examination had been ten years prior. In forensic psychiatry I tended to adopt a hands-off approach where possible. Violent, paranoid men generally don't like you in their personal space, far less making physical contact.

'Stand up, you're choking. Don't panic – I'm going to have to grab you from behind.'

I'd read about the Heimlich manoeuvre but had never performed it. I just went for it, wrapping my arms around him from behind and pulling backwards. The flow of air dislodged the sweetie, and it flew out of his mouth. Textbook. However, there was more drama to come. As I was performing the heroic, life-saving procedure (well, that's how I categorised it in my mind), a deluge of items cascaded out from under his jacket, including a toilet roll, paper towels and a citrus room spray. They were souvenirs from the staff toilet, acquired en route to the meeting. My somewhat embarrassed but less purple-faced patient promptly popped them back under his jacket and told us to carry on.

Talking of difficult patients, it's hard to say if there was one that could be described as the most challenging. Instead, I experienced a series of challenging situations that would ebb and flow in line with my patients' relapses. When they started to disengage, home visits could often be quite daunting, as it was unpredictable which colourful characters may burst into the flat while we were there or what vehement paranoid accusations our patients would make. It would become a particularly delicate verbal dance when addressing the issue of potential readmission to hospital. A large, ranting, psychotic man in a small flat can be pretty intimidating, and ten minutes can seem like an hour when you're waiting for a police escort to arrive. De-escalation techniques, distraction, humour, avoidance of contentious topics and loitering outside in the car park (to ensure they didn't flee the scene) all had their place. My staff needed to know that I always had their backs. Dealing with forensic patients in a community setting requires small caseloads so that staff can drop everything and respond immediately if there's any intelligence from family or other agencies that there's been a change in risk status. Public safety is paramount. After they experienced the responsiveness of our team, other agencies became supportive partners. They were more willing to allocate housing to patients with concerning histories because they were assured of the back-up available and the shared risk management plans in place. If we called the police to say 'We need help now', we tended to get it. The fact that we ran a free court liaison service 5 days a week, 52 weeks of the year, may have helped to develop that collaborative relationship.

I'd been tasked with setting up the court liaison service when I launched the forensic community mental health team, having previously set up the Glasgow service when I was a trainee at the Douglas Inch Centre. The idea was that if an offender who'd been picked up by the police the night before showed behaviour in the cells that was suggestive of possible acute mental illness, we'd assess them prior to them appearing in front of the sheriff. The service was offered free to the procurator fiscal. Essentially this was a safety net to try to catch acutely psychotic patients within the criminal justice system and remand them to hospital for assessment rather than to a prison environment. It didn't impact their need for prosecution. We provided a brief, handwritten report for the sheriff, having sorted out a bed for them in advance. It worked well. Along the way, I met a man whose 'normal' state was to walk backwards wearing a cowboy hat (according to the local psychiatrist); a woman claiming to be the Queen of Scotland; and a man who'd been hiding in a telephone box to avoid nanobots. Unfortunately, some people who are experiencing first-episode psychotic illness come to light through an offence, so court liaison provided an opportunity to assess them and link them into services. I'd also occasionally encounter acutely psychotic people who'd been misplaced in prison. One day, I was confronted by a woman who'd just thrown her child out of the window of a block of flats. Fortunately it's possible for psychiatrists to move prisoners to hospital in such circumstances, and in Scotland nearly all the forensic psychiatrists know each other. The process of finding a bed is easier when you're phoning a friend. There were some forms to complete and legal hoops to jump through, but I think we managed to transfer the woman out the next day.

High-profile cases often attract media attention, so media training comes in handy. During my career, I had two notable episodes involving courtroom skills and media training. On the first occasion, we received tips about doing interviews on TV or radio and were filmed being interviewed by a BBC journalist. After giving expert evidence in a mock courtroom, we were then cross-examined by a barrister from the Dr Harold Shipman case. Let's just say that I learnt a lot and just about survived, but some colleagues left in tears... it was pretty brutal. The next media training was an in-house event. During the coffee break, one of the trainers asked if they could have a quick word with me downstairs before the afternoon session. On arrival, I was doorstepped by a journalist and cameraman who stuck a big, furry microphone in my face. They asked me to comment on a controversial health board issue that had just hit the press. Now that's what I call impactful experiential learning. Role-play often freaks people out and is subsequently avoided by many, including myself. However, when I've been forced to do it, it has always provided a rich learning experience. Sadly, there was no such training available on how to survive the courtroom waiting room. If you inadvertently ended up in a room sitting cheek by jowl with the offender's pals, it could be extremely uncomfortable. I always sought out a room full of police officers and parked myself there. Maybe a bag of Werther's Originals would've helped.

CHAPTER 26

Cheese & Onion or Salt & Vinegar?

It wasn't always possible to do a full mental state examination. I was once asked to see a prisoner in her cell at Cornton Vale. Six staff appeared, wearing white paper bodysuits with hoods (an infection control measure, I believe), asking if I'd like one too. Since the suits had legs and I was wearing a skirt, I declined. The yetis and I, in my nice skirt suit, pearls and handbag, entered the cell. There was a mute prisoner hiding under a blanket, with urine slowly running across the floor towards me. All I knew was that she'd been remanded in custody after having been mute and aggressive in the community. She'd remained mute and had been throwing her urine at prison staff, so I was told to keep my distance. After a failed attempt at communication, I decided she needed to go to hospital for assessment and arranged the transfer, effectively detaining a blanket, as I didn't get any response out of her and saw nothing but her silhouette and her fast-approaching urine. If I was asked to see a suicidal prisoner, they were often wearing the 'Versace suit', which got its name because in Scotland 'Versace' rhymes with 'scratchy'. However, it doesn't quite have that haute couture look. Remember the anti-suicide suit we chose instead of the Dalek suit? That's the one. Sometimes the prisoner's behaviour had been so disturbed that the officers insisted that I communicated via the small hatch in the door, and remembered to stand back in case they fired urine or spat at me.

After the spate of suicides in 1996, which led to the longest fatal accident inquiry in Scottish legal history, changes were inevitable. The shell of the remand unit remained, but it was completely reconfigured. There was now a two-storey-high glass wall on one side of the building, which created a light, bright environment. Two tiers of cells lined the three remaining walls. The corridor outside the upstairs cells was a half-height glass partition that allowed a view into the central well of the open area below. This had a highly polished wood floor with fake trees. I did wonder how long it would be before someone was launched over the glass partition during a catfight. The officers were located behind a shiny wooden reception desk that wouldn't have looked out of place in a nice hotel. However, the staff behind it were more likely to restrain and floor you than call a porter to take your luggage. I marvelled at their skills because they were dealing with some of the most difficult, personality-disordered women in Scotland. The levels of self-harming behaviour were extreme. Staff were required to have a compassionate but boundaried approach, combined with a healthy dollop of Scottish humour, to cajole prisoners into complying with the prison regime and handing over 'banked' razor blades. There was often considerable negotiation involved. They were quick to notice when one of their revolving-door charges was unwell. They knew them so well that they could spot subtle changes in behaviour that signalled a deterioration in mental health and therefore increased risk.

'Could you have a word with Jeannie? She's no' right.'

We worked well together and trusted each other's

judgement. When I took student doctors with me, they said the prison was nicer than their halls of residence. But they didn't get to hear the screaming and banging that rang out overnight. The shiny new facade hid many damaged souls who sometimes tried to choke themselves with a tampon and bang their head against the concrete, incoherently muttering from behind a veil of straggly, unwashed hair. There are cynics out there who think that prisoners feign mental illness. You wouldn't be in any doubt if you met some of these troubled women. In my experience, it's hard to feign illness and sustain it, even if you have a detailed knowledge of symptoms. Thought disorder is probably the most difficult to feign and sustain over time. The main complicating factor for diagnosis is the increasing prevalence of drug-induced psychosis, often linked to amphetamines, cannabis or legal highs, as they can mimic illnesses such as schizophrenia. The practice of psychiatry has become all the more difficult as a result.

The nearest I ever came to experiencing psychiatric symptoms myself was during the Diploma in Forensic Medicine course, which I took during my maternity leave after Jill was born. One of the lectures was about scenes of crime. The lecturer shared an endless series of slides from their most horrific cases. At the time, I wasn't aware of feeling distressed or particularly horrified by them, but I did notice a couple of people leaving the lecture theatre early. I drove home afterwards, as usual. But when Richard began to talk to me, he seemed miles away and I felt quite detached from the room. Everything seemed unreal around me and felt distant and muffled. I think I was experiencing depersonalisation and derealisation, linked to the impact of the images I'd seen of brains dripping over the railway line after someone's head had been run over by a train.

In my role as associate medical director, I had to visit the relative of one of our inpatients after they'd absconded from the ward and jumped in front of a train. That was much more distressing. You may have encountered hallucinations in a family member, caused by physical illness when someone has a high temperature or metabolic disturbance, but the treatment will involve antibiotics, oxygen and fluids rather than psychiatric intervention. Our medical training ensured that we didn't misdiagnose physical illness as a psychiatric disorder.

When Mum had major heart surgery, she complained about the dog belonging to the patient in the next bed, which she said had kept her awake all night with its barking. When the doctor did her ward round, Mum tried to rip the central line out of her neck and kicked the female doctor in the groin. My clean-living, Sunday school teacher mum was mortified when she found out later. My role as her daughter/doctor was to report that Mum had had auditory and visual hallucinations of a barking dog and suggest that they check her blood gases. Some oxygen and a further period of ventilation solved the problem. I knew my medical training would come in handy one day! However, we didn't get first aid training at medical school, so if you ever need help in an emergency, don't ask me for assistance.

The importance of identifying other potential causes for symptoms was brought home to me as a senior trainee in the intensive psychiatric ward when, during a patient interview in a quiet room, I started to hear a muffled male voice that clearly wasn't my patient's.

'Did you hear that?'

'No. Are you hearing voices too, doctor?'

After a few puzzling moments, he was delighted to reveal his talking watch. He may have been psychotic, but he hadn't lost his sense of humour.

Whether I was assessing patients in the community, the ward or in prison, it was important to remember one thing: patients do not exist in isolation. When you drop a pebble in a pool, it doesn't just go plop and sink; it causes a ripple effect. And that's how it is with mental illness. Those around the patient, whether it be staff, fellow patients, prisoners, family, friends, colleagues or neighbours, will all be impacted directly or indirectly. For me, being a daughter, doctor, psychiatrist, wife and mum all at the same time often became complicated, especially when there was a clash of roles. They inevitably overlapped and created a collision of ripples. A relapse or incident involving one of my patients might mean turning up late to pick up the kids from school, or having to go into work at the weekend to do a court report, which meant missing a swimming gala.

When Fraser was 13, we attended parents' night at his school. It was held in the dining hall, with tables set out in neat rows, the teacher on one side and three chairs opposite. It was a carefully orchestrated affair, with timetabled slots, each family moving seamlessly from one subject teacher to another every few minutes. In reality, groups of parents were hovering like vultures around the most popular subject tables, hoping to jump into the hot seats. Fraser, Richard and I had just hovered and landed at the English teacher's table when my phone rang.

'I'm so sorry, I'm on call for work, please excuse me.'

'Police here. Are you the on-call psychiatrist? We've got a gun siege involving a man with schizophrenia. We need you to come and advise the police negotiators.'

Fraser and Richard were still with the English teacher when I returned to the hall.

'Sorry, I have to leave. I'm needed at a gun siege.'

Three alarmed faces stared back at me. It wasn't the sort of thing that normally happened during parents' night at a private school. I stopped off at the ward en route, collecting a nurse who knew the patient. When we arrived, the street was already cordoned off, with several police vehicles in attendance. The neighbours were out in their pyjamas, wrapped in blankets and drinking Irn-Bru, not wanting to miss the unfolding drama. Having identified ourselves to the police, we were told to park the car on a piece of disused land round the corner and await instructions. Several police officers spilled out of a van in the street opposite, silhouetted by the streetlights, and removed a large holdall from the back of the van.

Me: 'What do you think's in the bag? Guns?'

My colleague: 'Look, they're taking something shiny out of the bag. It's definitely guns. What's he doing? What's that? It's a folding child's scooter! He's riding up and down the pavement. What's going on?'

Our attention was diverted by the arrival of a policeman at the car window, requesting that we attend the local police station to talk to the patient's mother. We never did discover the significance of the scooter. After meeting with his mother, we returned to the scene and were allowed through the cordon. We were instructed to park outside the house adjoining the patient's house, presumably out of gunshot range. We were now players in the unfolding drama and subject to the speculation of the pyjama crew. The police had guns, dogs and negotiators and every so often we were required to wind down the window to give advice to the negotiators, advising them about how a psychotic man might respond in this particular situation. After an hour or so, a senior police officer with stripes and shiny buttons approached the car.

Much to our surprise, he hoisted up a carrier bag and put it through the passenger window.

'Help yourselves. There's sandwiches, crisps and juice.'

The toughest decision of a stressful evening: was it to be cheese and onion or salt and vinegar? By 2 pm, we'd reached a stalemate and were stood down. The patient eventually emerged the next morning, without incident. It was certainly more exciting than parents' night.

There were three other times when I had to report outpatients who allegedly had a firearm. One of these involved being called to join the police incident team as they were planning how to safely deal with the situation. I had mixed emotions about my experience. On the one hand, I was frustrated by how long it seemed to take to mobilise a response to attend the location as I feared my psychotic patient might have left and may now be wandering in the community with a gun. On the other hand, I was incredibly impressed by the professionalism, strategic organisation and attention to detail of my police colleagues. Fortunately, there were no incidents where anyone was hurt, and the therapeutic relationships survived my need to breach confidentiality. As always, I explained my reasons, but continued to offer support afterwards. Looking back at these different situations, I'm reminded that, when forced to make choices, we have to consider many factors. They'll be impacted by the multiple roles that we hold simultaneously. There's rarely a right answer, but on balance one action may be more favourable or less risky than another. The overarching decider must be positive intent, and that's what has always driven my response to clinical situations as well as to life. It isn't always as straightforward as choosing a bag of crisps.

CHAPTER 27

Kill Me and Take My Organs

There was a thick frost on the bedroom window and the pavements outside were glistening with ice. I had to go to work on my day off, as finding a Russian interpreter to do a court report hadn't been easy. I had to assess an educated Russian man who'd been arrested as an illegal immigrant and was facing deportation. It was so cold inside that you could see your breath in the air. This was going to take some time, so frostbite felt like a distinct possibility. A normal court report assessment took about 90 minutes; this one took closer to four hours because of the interpreter delay. The man's detailed, heart-rending story involved a series of concerning events at work and the death of a colleague, which led him to conclude that the KGB were involved and he may be the next target. He left everything and fled the country by train and boat, eventually ending up in Scotland before being apprehended some months later. He believed that if he was deported, he'd be killed before leaving the airport. He didn't appear to be psychotic but had some symptoms suggestive of PTSD that may have benefited from treatment. Returning to Russia was likely to be detrimental to his mental health as it would potentially trigger his symptoms (not to mention potential risk to his physical wellbeing and survival). It was difficult not to feel his anguish.

Before we finished, I asked, 'Is there anything else you want to tell me that you think is important?' The interpreter relayed his response: 'Can you kill me and take my organs? I want my life to mean something.' How do you answer that? Obviously, I didn't kill him or offer him an organ donor card, but I did offer to attend his deportation hearing in Glasgow to support his case to remain. The proceedings were surreal, with senior clergy from the Russian Orthodox church, in full robes and crosses, arguing on his behalf. Meeting people from different countries and cultures was always challenging, as it's hard to comprehend what life is like in a communist state or a war zone full of rebels carrying out terrorist attacks. It's so far removed from my stable Scottish upbringing, with its freedom of speech and movement.

As a psychiatrist, it's also important to clarify whether an unusual belief is a delusional false belief or whether it's a shared cultural or religious one. For example, in Scotland, possession by devils would be quite an unusual belief, suggestive of a paranoid psychotic illness, but it may be how people verbalise physical ill health in a third world country. In Scotland we saw Rangers, Celtic and the freemasons incorporated into delusional systems. At Christmas, we often had more than one Jesus in the ward. When Jesus headed to A&E to cure the sick, we usually received a call to go and collect him. To ensure that the beliefs were not shared cultural ones, it was vital to check out potential delusions with the family. We occasionally encountered a disorder called *folie à deux*, where a family member shared the same delusional belief. Trying to explain to a father that you wouldn't be referring his daughter to the surgeons to have the transmitter removed from her left eye was awkward when the father believed it was in there too. Invoking the Mental Health Act to prevent them from leaving the country to have it operated on privately was equally complicated. We were taught to acknowledge the patient's distress but not to collude with their delusions, so a parent reinforcing them could be detrimental to recovery.

Sometimes it was blindingly obvious that someone had a mental illness. When someone tells you 'I've got a dead rat in my stomach – I can smell it rotting inside me', you're clearly dealing with a symptom. My trainee psychiatrist didn't discuss this case with me after the ward round, but the patient's delusional beliefs and olfactory (smell) hallucinations had quite an impact on him. Before Christmas, the trainee appeared at my office door, saying, 'I've got a Christmas present for you, Dr Morrison.' Thanking him, I opened my gift and found a hand-painted glass tumbler with a picture of a dancing girl on its side. I sat it on my desk as a pencil holder. A month or so later, when dictating a report, my eyes lifted towards the glass. There, clear as day, was a girl wearing a jumper. The design on the jumper was a circle with a rat inside.

That same patient had made an altogether different impression on me. I'd been her doctor for years. One day, on my birthday, I joked with her at the ward round:

'I'm disappointed in you.'

'Why, doctor?'

'It's my birthday and you didn't sing "Happy Birthday"... You just can't get the patients these days.'

It was just a bit of banter between two people who'd known each other for a number of years.

'Dr Morrison, if I'd known it was your birthday, I'd have baked you a cake.'

We laughed together and she left the ward round. Two hours later there was a knock at the door. I was still seeing patients.

'Dr Morrison, I made you a cake and a card over at the OT department.'

My slice of cake was neatly presented on a side plate,

alongside my card. That kind gesture made more of an impression on me than the rat in her stomach. Over the years I'd supported her through a multitude of personal and family tragedies, so I'd probably also fulfilled the role of maternal figure, and that was clearly not all about medication. However, the treatment offered in this low-secure ward wasn't focused exclusively on medication as many of our patients had drug-resistant illness. They were never completely symptom free. Attempting to deliver holistic care means covering all aspects of quality of life, which may ultimately have a positive impact on a patient's mental health. It's all about finding ways to live with your illness (and the rat).

At one point, following an audit in the ward, we wrote a paper for the health board that tried to capture the change in patient population and associated risk factors over a ten-year period. We were looking for more staff to support staffed socialisation, a wider range of psychological therapies and risk testing outside the ward, as well as increased security in the garden area. The population was now younger, had a higher incidence of drug-resistant psychosis, impulsivity, aggression, offending, deliberate self-harm and substance misuse. The multidisciplinary team had been increased to include a forensic psychiatrist, nurses, clinical forensic psychologist, occupational therapist, music therapist, art therapist, dietician and pharmacist, supported by a visiting GP, mental health social worker and chaplain. When we listed the various treatment options, my quirky sense of humour slipped out. I just had to add maggot therapy to the list, as we'd been advised by the clinic at the general hospital to use live maggots to treat a patient's leg ulcer. It probably wasn't a standard treatment offered in other forensic psychiatric units!

The beauty of a long-term relationship with a forensic patient means that you also get to see their long-term circle of life. Even patients with a drug-resistant illness who are never totally symptom free may eventually achieve discharge to the community, where the forensic service continues to support them. At my last outpatient appointment before I retired, one of my patients arrived with chocolates and flowers as well as his new baby, the proud father showing off his offspring to his substitute mum. Patients may still experience breakthrough symptoms but can be quite inspirational, even in adversity. I left that clinic with a feeling of pride.

CHAPTER 28

To Restrain or Not to Restrain, That Is the Question

'**D**r Morrison, we need urgent assistance. Your patient's smashed all the unbreakable glass windows in the ward with a table and he's swinging a cord with a plug around his head. We can't get anywhere near him to restrain him.'

'Where are you?'

'Under the desk, locked in the office!'

I coordinated a response from the front seat of my car while sitting in a car park. My patient ended up being admitted to the high-secure State Hospital. Unusually, following that admission, it was concluded that if he presented to the police in a psychotic state in future, he should be held in police custody until being assessed by a psychiatrist for consideration for direct admission due to risk of extreme violence.

It was the emergency phone calls that we all dreaded. You had to think on your feet, immediately reorganise your diary and ramp up into emergency response mode. You didn't quite know what would confront you when you got there; the only certainty was that you needed to respond NOW!

Someone called the office, screaming at my secretary that they were terrified. 'He's trying to strangle me. Aaaagh!'

The phone call ended with a blood-curdling scream, then it cut off. My PA interrupted me in the middle of my outpatient clinic. I had no choice but to leave and deal with the emergency as a priority, so one of the community nurses stepped in to see the remaining outpatients. We didn't know my patient's location, but had some intelligence that they were living in a caravan outside our health board area. I contacted the local police station and asked them to assist by going to the caravan park and trying to locate our patient, uncertain as to what they might find, or if the victim would still be alive. The patient's past illness and offending history suggested that the risk was significant. Two nurses came with me in my car, armed with some intramuscular antipsychotic tranquilliser. We headed for the police station, having agreed to meet the police there to assess the patient, if they could locate him. He was unlikely to come quietly. By the time we arrived, the police had located and apprehended him.

'He's too agitated, doctor. It's not safe for you to go into the cell with him.'

Dignity issues were certainly not at the top of the police officers' list of priorities. For everyone's safety they insisted that the patient be held in police restraint and brought out into an open area in the police station, where they removed his trousers and exposed his buttock so that my nurse colleagues could administer an injection. We then had to wait for half an hour to allow the medication to kick in before we could assess him. The good news was that his victim had survived. Patients who have unstable accommodation or just seem to move around a lot are difficult to monitor, support and manage. In my view, stable accommodation in a suitable area is absolutely crucial to positive outcomes as it allows access to local support agencies, which are almost all delineated by postcode. The frustration we experienced when a patient lived on the boundary between two health board areas cannot be overestimated: 'He's not in our catchment, sorry, can't help you.'... repeat, repeat... I would've loved to have spoken to a pragmatic human being who was actually person centred.

The use of restraints for behaviourally disturbed patients was always a controversial topic. I remember visiting services in Canada and the USA, where mechanical restraints were still in use. I was horrified, but they argued that our practice of using major tranquillisation medication and three-person restraint teams was equally barbaric. Our staff had specialist de-escalation, control and restraint training and protocols for safe use of emergency sedation when patients were behaviourally disturbed, but the reality is that patients sometimes come to harm during a physical restraint. When a musclebound, psychotic man is headbutting the door, screaming at the top of their voice and has smashed up the furniture in their room, it doesn't quite match the well-controlled training room scenario. Tensions are high, staff and the other patients are probably fearful of getting assaulted and the pressure is on to intervene before they hurt themselves or anyone else.

Across the country there's evidence that patient deaths have occurred as a result of poorly managed restraints, when chest wall movement has been compromised due to the position in which they've been held, or cardiac arrhythmias have occurred due to high doses of medication being administered, particularly intramuscularly. Patients who fight with staff experience increased blood flow to their muscles and as a result high doses of medication are absorbed more quickly into the bloodstream. Our service introduced a standardised post-restraint debrief process, linked to the patient safety programme, aimed at staff and patient reflection and learning. Had we noted and acted on early warning signs that could perhaps have avoided escalation to the point of requiring physical restraint? Did we follow health board policy regarding control and restraint and emergency sedation? Were all staff up to date with refresher training in these areas? Did the patient have an opportunity to discuss the incident once settled? Had patients who may have witnessed the situation been debriefed? You can't underestimate the emotional impact of being physically restrained by three staff, particularly if you have a history of abuse. It could be re-traumatising. Physical restraint is not for the timid, but when de-escalation and above-maximum doses of sedation haven't worked, there's often no choice. A gender mix of staff often has a calming influence, which we also noticed in the prison setting. As the intensive psychiatric care unit consultant for several years, I often had to get involved in these patient management debates.

In the outpatient setting there was no three-man team. De-escalation was your main technique for dealing with difficult situations. As a consultant I was forced to revisit my learning about sitting near the door and the perils of taking a sexual history. Having learnt from my encounter with Superman, I was now seeing new patients with a colleague, in this case our new female mental health officer social worker.

It was a case of 'lewd and libidinous behaviour and indecent exposure of his private member to the lieges' (flashing in the park). To avoid giving the address of our team base to potentially violent offenders, who might turn up unannounced when our administrative staff were alone in the building, we always booked a room in the nearest local community hospital or GP surgery. Unfortunately, the interview room was along a winding corridor and tucked away in a corner. Are you noticing a pattern? We always seemed to get the riskiest environment to interview the riskiest patients! It was a long, rectangular room, with a door and a seat at one end and two seats and a desk at the other. This invited staff to sit at the far end, with the patient in the single seat next to the door, which was not ideal. Staff should always be nearer the door to allow for a safe exit. The office staff had been unable to find the panic alarm, but we'd decided to go ahead anyway, which proved to be a crucial error. Early on in the assessment, it became clear that our patient was distracted, maybe thought disordered, and possibly psychotic. In my head, I was contemplating discussing an inpatient assessment with the social worker before providing a report for the court. As it was a sexual offence, I had to take a sexual history. Asking about masturbatory fantasies isn't part of most people's jobs, but occasionally it featured in mine. He suddenly stood up, dropped his jeans and started to masturbate his erect penis. I stood up, saying to myself, 'Keep calm... keep calm, Rhona.'

'What are you doing? Put that away and sit down.'

I turned to my colleague: '25?'

This was the number of a section of the Mental Health Act and summed up all of my panicked internal dialogue. It would allow us to detain him in hospital for assessment. My colleague nodded, having been thinking the same thing. As the patient sat down, glazed and bewildered, we moved swiftly to the door. We had to summon help, call the police and fill in detention paperwork. Before we could agree on how to coordinate this safely, he stood up and started masturbating again, obviously preoccupied by something. He then moved across the room and tried to weigh himself on the eating disorder clinic's scales. Clinic staff responded quickly, and the police arrived about 40 minutes later. We asked for assistance to transport him to hospital.

'Oh, we didn't bring a van, we'll go and get one.' The police station was quite nearby, so I think they'd walked.

'One of you can go and get the van,' I replied. 'I think one of you should stay here with us!'

The fact that we had a potentially psychotic sex offender who had just offended again, in an outpatient clinic full of vulnerable, mentally ill patients, appeared to have escaped their notice. We had to evacuate the waiting area and move him to a less cramped environment, with a male nurse acting as his minder while we completed the legal paperwork and gave a statement. It could have ended very differently. The fact that I had him charged with the offence did not prevent me from treating him, but the potential conflict of interest was declared to the court. In cases like this, when a first-episode illness presents with offending, we were always required to collect additional sources of information. It often became clear that there'd been evidence of a developing psychotic illness for many months leading up to the offences. There may have been gradual social withdrawal, poor self-care, deterioration in academic performance and odd behaviours such as lining a baseball cap with tinfoil, blacking out windows in an attempt to block toxic rays from the glass factory or something equally bizarre. Families confronted by the first episode of psychotic illness are often valiantly trying to cope with a loved one who's acting bizarrely, and they don't know what's happening or how to access help.

Sometimes, patients who committed serious offences while unwell became the greatest success stories. Mental illness can affect anyone, and people from a good, supportive family may become unwell and commit an illness-related offence before coming to the attention of services. It's not common for people with mental illness to offend, but in forensic psychiatry we saw a disproportionate number of those who offended when unwell, as they're more likely to be risky and need closer monitoring in the community. There's a risk of illness relapse and further offending. This outpatient situation reinforced the importance of security alarms, two staff for new assessments and sitting nearest the door. Mental illness can make good people behave badly. My job was to find the good people, treat them, manage risk and get them functioning normally again.

However, the behavioural changes associated with illness relapse were not always as obvious as someone smashing up the ward or masturbating in my office. Do you remember the Tom and Jerry cartoons, and how Tom would run through walls, leaving a Tom-shaped hole in the brickwork? We had a similar incident with one of our patients. We discovered that he'd hacked a person-shaped door in the back of his house, hidden inside a cupboard, just in case he needed to escape. This caused significant concern. Paranoid, insightless patients don't always report illness relapse, so noticing odd behaviour is key. Our staff could have been detectives because they were always on the hunt for clues, hence the cupboard check. Alcohol consumption was best gauged from the bottles in the wheelie bin rather than from self-report, and self-care checks might mean noticing if the level of shower gel had gone down since last month or if there was a car tyre sitting in the bath, which would suggest showering was not at the top of their priority list. Sometimes the pieces of the jigsaw only fell into place at the team meeting, when seemingly unimportant observations and collateral information from different staff added together to suggest a rising concern. One missed appointment, failure to collect a prescription, a sighting when intoxicated outside a nightclub or a call from family to report a threatening altercation may suggest disengagement and early relapse, worthy of a wee home visit from the local forensic team.

In due course we were informed that our team was going to be relocated, to save money. We ended up moving to a disused psychogeriatric ward on the community hospital site, which was musty and smelled of urine. The building was shared with a GP surgery and the staff bank, which dealt with locum nurses. We all had different ideas about the security of the building. We seemed to be the only team trying to keep people out. The other staff would hold the door to let visitors enter and buzz strangers through. We were worried that violent, psychotic men or stalkers may follow staff and threaten the secretaries when we were all out on home visits or at local clinics. Our patients were on an exclusive 'call me on this number' basis because we didn't give out our address. After a few educational chats with other services, we were going to require a buzzer and keypad entry.

CHAPTER 29

Merry Christmas, Dr Morrison

In his role as president of the school alumni society, Fraser had invited me to give a lecture about mental health awareness. My suggestion for a slightly edgy, controversial title was thrown out, and we eventually agreed on something much more sedate: 'Tackling stigma in mental illness'. It was advertised on social media in an attempt to attract former pupils, and the school subsequently received a call from a student at Edinburgh University requesting permission to attend. He was thinking of changing course and thought that it might be interesting. It wasn't a closed event, so they agreed.

It was already dark when I arrived for the pre-talk drinks reception. Crossing the puddled playground, I noticed a tall, thin man in a dark hoodie standing near the hall where the lecture would be taking place. I assumed he was the student, as I was familiar with most of the parents and pupils. It was a small school of only 300 or so pupils, and my children had attended for a total of 13 years between them. Socialising over, we made our way to the hall. With an audience of about 60 people, who were on tiered seating, there was no need for the sound system. I planned to stand at the lectern and use PowerPoint to illustrate my lecture, which was scheduled to last about an hour. Having made a point of scanning the audience, I saw a sea of smiling, familiar faces. There was no sign of the hoodie man. I began, as usual, by explaining that the term forensic psychiatrist doesn't mean that I talk to dead bodies, but that I work with mentally disordered offenders. Twelve minutes into my talk, I was interrupted by a loud crackling noise that sounded like interference on the sound system, except that it wasn't turned on. A man could be heard ranting unintelligibly in a loud voice. It seemed to go on forever, so I had to stop the lecture.

The headmaster left to investigate. The ranting stopped, so I resumed my lecture, now with the distraction of internal dialogue, wondering, 'Which of my patients are ill at present? Could someone have followed me? Who did I see this morning?' But I drew a blank. I attempted to stay focused and tried to deliver witty anecdotes to illustrate my talk – but not for long. The crackling started again. The voice was behind me, but there was no one there. More people left to investigate and there were lots of confused glances. The ranting stopped again, but not before I heard a muffled 'Merry Christmas, Dr Morrison.' This was clearly not a coincidence. This was deliberately directed at me, and it didn't feel good. I kept going until the end of the hour and there was warm applause. The headmaster hadn't returned after the initial interruption, and in my peripheral vision I saw men in high-vis jackets through the glass panels of the gym hall doors. There was a vote of thanks, and I received a beautiful Christmas flower arrangement. Then there was an announcement: 'The police are outside and have advised that no one should leave the hall without an escort, for their own safety.'

A muttering swept through the audience. Some people clearly thought I had set this up to make my lecture more intriguing, but the rest of us were worried. For the first time in my career, I felt genuinely rattled. I've had patients pull out a knife in my office, attempt to throw a bookcase out of a first-floor window, masturbate during an assessment and bring a machete hidden in the sleeve of their anorak, but this was personal. This was my children's school. This was a planned offence targeted at me.

Heart pounding and stomach churning, I requested an escort to my car and checked under the car and the tyres before I got in. To ensure that I wasn't being followed, I kept looking in my mirror as I drove home. The next day, the school confirmed that they'd found a walkie talkie under the grand piano in the hall, to the left and behind where I'd been standing. The hall's fire door was ajar. A member of staff reported that, before the talk, a man in a hoodie had asked if he could film the talk and put leaflets on the seats, but they declined.

There was a police investigation at the school, but no one interviewed me, so I never found out what happened or who had done it. As the weeks passed, it gradually faded from my memory. Many months later, a former patient contacted the team to raise a concern as she'd found about 200 videos on YouTube made by her ex-boyfriend, some of which included distressing content in relation to me. I'd met him once many years before when, as a potential named victim, I'd tried to alert him of a risk to his safety. I was trying to help him, but he didn't see it that way. He was not my patient. His girlfriend ended their relationship at that point, and he blamed me. He left multiple messages on our answering machine at work, blaming me for ruining his life. They only stopped when we threatened to go to the police.

We went online right away to check out the videos. Going onto YouTube was daunting. Nothing could have prepared me for what I was about to see. A creepy, gaunt young man stared back at me from a homemade video, saying 'Dr Morrison's a black hole.' What does that even mean? It felt cold, empty and sinister, sending a shiver right through me. In another video I saw 'DR MORRISON IS A LIAR' written in lipstick on the glass door of one of the hospital buildings. I spotted one that was filmed outside the outpatient clinic where we'd first met, saying he was back there on the anniversary of the day I'd ruined his life. The shiver was back. It's hard to articulate the feelings I experienced following the realisation that this man had been obsessed with me for about a decade. Then we discovered the video that captured his preparation for the incident when he interrupted my lecture at my children's old school. The enormity of the situation started to dawn on me. This man was filled with hatred towards me, and this had now escalated to stalking and offending. I was traumatised by the content. I couldn't watch all of it. The emotional impact was overwhelming. This man had crossed the invisible line surrounding my professional life, invading my personal, family space. My colleagues were great, offering to sift through the videos and look for anything of relevance. My memories of that time are mostly fragments as I was too upset to take it all in.

If there's one thing I have learnt in forensic psychiatry, it's to trust my instincts (gut feelings are usually spot on in terms of assessing danger). If you feel a situation is unsafe, get out. It may be an obvious visible or verbal threat or a more subtle clue, picked up by the subconscious, but my internal radar rarely let me down. I felt a strong, visceral sensation in the pit of my stomach. I watched as he debated whether to purchase a baby monitor or walkie talkie to disrupt my lecture. Fast forward to a video of the dark, wet school playground, recorded a few metres away from the alumni drinks reception. I was oblivious to the drama unfolding outside. He then filmed himself entering the hall to plant the walkie talkie under the grand piano at the back of the hall and sprinkled some shortbread crumbs on the lectern to let me know he'd been there. It was upsetting to watch. These acts were clearly carried out with malicious intent to cause emotional distress. The disruption of the lecture was an attempt to discredit me. Heart pounding against the walls of my chest, I called Richard. 'Can you give Fraser a lift? I need to go to police headquarters after work to report a stalker. We've discovered hundreds of videos on YouTube. It's him that disrupted my lecture at the school last year.'

That first interview with the police is also a bit of a blur. I gave a garbled account of the historical context, the disrupted lecture months earlier, and our discovery of the evidence on YouTube. I tried to impress upon them my professional concern about my stalker's escalation to offending after all this time. I was reassured to hear that I'd be visited at home to give a full statement to the investigating officers. They were brilliant, taking a detailed account of the evidence. They were sensitive about the emotional impact it had had on me, and reassured me that they'd investigate with a view to prosecution. A multi-agency investigation and response was about to crank into action.

The sequence and timeline of events are muddled in my head, with everything moving quickly over a matter of days. I found myself dealing with the NHS corporate management team, the Medical and Dental Defence Union for Scotland (MDDUS), specialist lawyers with experience in stalking legislation, Police Scotland, the cybercrime unit, hospital security and the court. My general manager organised for hospital security to be ramped up within half an hour of our chat. A plan was put in place overnight to install a secure, push-button door entry system for the management team suite where I was now based, to prevent strangers (or stalkers) having open access to my office. Visitors would now have to liaise with admin staff before being permitted entry. Another manager presented me with two personal security alarms. Everyone became more vigilant, especially checking the car park next to our clinical team office, and we were asked to report any suspicious activity. We shared the building with a local GP practice, so the receptionists were asked to report anyone asking for Dr Morrison.

The MDDUS were quick to identify the need for specialist lawyers and, within two days, I was sitting in a legal office in Glasgow, recounting my tale for the umpteenth time. They liaised directly with the police, allowing a coordinated approach because the cybercrime unit wanted to get the evidence off YouTube, and the police wanted to raid the stalker's home to gather electronic devices as evidence before he knew that they were on to him. The videos of him planning and committing his offence against me at the lecture were pretty crucial to the case. It became a tense waiting game. I became intensely aware of my personal security, constantly scanning the area around me when leaving the building to get to my car. Trees, parked cars and shadows all felt sinister. I wondered if he was lurking, ready to pounce. Opening the car door, jumping in and putting the locks on became a frenzied process. Only then could I relax. Having met my stalker all those years before, I had some cause for concern regarding his mental health. Thankfully, the police agreed to inform the court of the need for a mental health assessment, which may have been important for disposal options if convicted.

I'm really proud of the professionalism of my team, who were asked to carry out the assessment of my stalker. During our weekly team meetings, we'd normally feed back the outcome of any assessments carried out the previous week and discuss potential disposal. Despite being one of the lead clinicians, I was asked to leave the meeting as they were going to discuss the outcome of my stalker's assessment. It was important to maintain his confidentiality, and they also wanted to protect me as the victim. The significant investment in staff training had definitely paid off. I had total faith in their assessment and management of any identified risk.

So much evidence had been collected from YouTube and the offender's home that, when the case came to court, I didn't have to attend. He was found guilty of breach of the peace and stalking in both the civil and criminal court as some of his behaviour pre-dated the introduction of stalking legislation. My home was flagged on the police computer in case I called for assistance, and a five-year non-harassment order was put in place. I wanted to be able to call for assistance if he was anywhere near me, not after he had done something, so this gave me some comfort. A Scottish non-harassment order is a formal court order granted by a sheriff court. The harassment must have occurred on at least two occasions and have caused distress and alarm. The social media material, phone calls and stalking behaviour all counted. Richard never quite understood why I was so upset.

'You know he's probably unwell; that's the kind of work you do.'

I never expected to find myself in *The Sun* newspaper, but there I was, in a photo of me and my stalker.

CHAPTER 30

I Want to Kill My Sister

The forensic team had received some intelligence to suggest that one of our outpatients was taking illicit drugs and probably becoming psychotic again. He'd stripped naked and was threatening to kill a family member (who thankfully wasn't at home), and was ranting incoherently in his bedroom. It was time for a friendly home visit. We arranged to meet round the corner from the house to agree on a plan of action. A rapid response was clearly necessary in such circumstances, which meant that managing my diary was crucial. We went armed with detention papers, just in case hospital admission would be required, as it would probably be against his will. Having agreed on our strategy, we approached the front door. We could hear shouting coming from inside the house. A man answered but signalled for us to be careful. At the top of the stairs, our half-dressed patient was ranting loudly in our direction.

'F*** off, get out! What are you doing here?'

'We just popped round to see how you were getting on because you missed your last...'

'F**k off!'

He stayed upstairs, went into a bedroom and slammed the door. The nurse and I sneaked into the living room where, in hushed tones, we tried to establish what had been happening. The man had been experiencing distressing visual hallucinations and was preoccupied by some sort of conspiracy theory. He came thundering down the stairs and stood over us, ranting in our direction. Sitting on the couch, we weren't best placed for a rapid exit. We acknowledged the distress he was in, but didn't reinforce his delusional or hallucinatory experiences. Then he announced that he wanted to kill his sister. She'd become incorporated into his paranoid delusional system. He started to stare at the nurse sitting next to me on the couch, saying that he believed she'd been replaced by his sister. It was time to get out. De-escalation of the situation was in order.

'I sense our presence here is upsetting you. That wasn't our intention. We just popped in to see how you were doing. We're going to leave now.' (Subtext: to call the police. And then, just like Arnold Schwarzenegger, we'll be back.)

The police had provided welcome back-up on a number of occasions, particularly when we'd told reluctant patients they needed to go to hospital. On this occasion, we huddled in the car, out of sight, discussed the proposed detention with the mental health social worker and called the police for assistance. We had to go back to inform the patient that he was being detained under the Mental Health Act, and the mental health social worker tried to explain his rights to him. Having to conduct a conversation with an angry, psychotic man while he's hiding upstairs isn't ideal. Eventually, after a stand-off at the door, he was escorted to hospital by the police in his vest, jogging bottoms, bare feet and handcuffs.

While management of violence and aggression training are still mandatory, the training for NHS doctors includes light-touch breakaway and de-escalation techniques. This is because control and restraint techniques require three staff and aren't much use while working single-handedly in an outpatient setting. Prison training was a different kettle of fish altogether. As a visiting psychiatrist, I had to do the full training. Trainees were encouraged to go for kicks, punches and restraints. We had big protector pads, but you still felt the impact. Sitting astride the male chaplain during one restraint role-play scenario didn't feel altogether comfortable but, in the end, talking my way out of a situation was always the de-escalation technique that worked for me. On one occasion, at Cornton Vale, they let me use the interview room in the corridor outside the main residential hall. They usually kept the adjoining door open and there were officers in close proximity, but not actually in the room. Given that we were required to sit near the door, the fact that the panic button was on the wall above the far side of the desk was a problem. That day, a prison officer had entered the unit to collect other prisoners and automatically locked the internal door behind him, locking me and the prisoner in an isolated corridor outside the unit. Normally that wouldn't have been much of an issue, but this was a new prisoner who was psychotic. She was loud and animated, standing up, leaning across the desk towards me.

'I've been stung by a million bees.'

She hoisted up her top to reveal her naked chest and abdomen, to show me the non-existent proof. Such was the level of her frustration and irritability that spit was flying across the desk and hitting me in the face. I tried to look concerned, but didn't challenge her statement. I was thinking, 'How am I going to get her back to the hall without getting assaulted?' She was becoming increasingly agitated. I thought officers would hear her shouting and intervene, but no one came. It wasn't safe to lean towards an irate woman in an attempt to reach the emergency buzzer.

'I can see you're really quite upset by all of this. I'm going to go out for a moment and get someone to help.'

That was when I discovered the lock-in situation. I tried knocking on the door but there were no officers in the vicinity.

She was becoming more animated and irritable. I went back in and tried to de-escalate the situation again, but was unsuccessful. Eventually, after what seemed like a lifetime (in reality, about ten minutes), there was a knock at the door.

'Everything all right in here?'

My wide eyes and raised eyebrows communicated my predicament. Assistance was summoned; crisis averted. It was a further reminder that an incorrect room layout can put you in a dangerous position, and we always had to be nearest the door to avoid getting trapped or barricaded in by a prisoner. It was a difficult one to resolve.

Fortunately, some patients and their families appreciated the input from our team and were not prone to ranting at us or threatening violence. What does the gift of a giant tomato say about the doctor-patient relationship? Not a lot, in isolation, but when you know what it means, you'll understand. Receiving my patient's prize tomato said it all. She valued the team's input so much that she wanted me to have it as a thank-you. She'd been so paranoid when we first met that she used to have someone parked outside the outpatient clinic, with the car engine running, just in case she needed to make a quick escape. It was gratifying to see her gradually build trust in our team and develop meaningful engagement. Seeing patients begin to embrace new ways of thinking and behaving and no longer resolving conflict with violence was extremely gratifying. After attending a cognitive and behavioural skills group for high-risk recidivists, one man had such a lightbulb moment that he taught the skills he'd learnt to the men in the pub that night.

Before I retired, I had to hand over my patients to my replacement.

Patient: 'What am I going to do now? If I get angry and want to fight, I say to myself, "Dr Morrison wouldn't like it. Don't let her down".'

New consultant: 'Why don't you just keep saying that? It seems to be working for you.'

They warmed to the new doctor after she said that. I was witnessing my legacy in action.

CHAPTER 31

Dealing with Difficult Patients... and Colleagues

At this point I need to tell you about a pivotal moment that took place when I was on call during my training days. The pager flashed as I woke from a light sleep. It was an emergency call to the psychiatric rehabilitation ward. That was quite unusual, as the patients there have usually passed the acute phase of illness. I pulled on a jumper over my scrub PJs and quickly headed out into the cold, frosty morning. I ran through the trees and up the path towards the large building that housed the rehab unit. I discovered the emergency lying on the icy path in front of me. The crumpled body of a woman had hit the ground hard after she'd jumped from the roof. She was surrounded by distressed nursing staff, frozen in shock, waiting for me to take control of the situation. A long-term patient with chronic schizophrenia shuffled past, looking for cigarette butts, not really appreciating the seriousness of the tableau confronting him. They don't prepare you for this sort of situation at medical school. It was time to man up, as they say.

It was too early for any consultants to be at work, so I was all they had. Adrenaline kicked in, and it didn't take me long to establish that resuscitation wouldn't be required. I dispatched nurses to fetch screens to protect her dignity. Our audience member was redirected to his own ward, and I called the police. Technically, this was a suspicious, non-accidental death in a hospital. I thought that meant we needed to protect the crime scene, until the police said otherwise. Awaiting the arrival of the police, I headed into the ward to offer support to the staff and any patients who were aware of what had happened. I expected to be offered a nerve-calming cup of tea and some support, but instead a nurse thrust a telephone into my hand. Covering the mouthpiece, she said, 'Mrs X's relative is on the phone asking how she is today.' Mrs X was lying outside, dead on the path, probably having committed suicide. Time to grow up.

I asked myself, 'How would I want someone to talk to me if I was a relative in such a situation?' I chose to tell the truth, shared with compassion and a willingness to answer questions as openly and honestly as possible, and I've adopted that approach ever since. It has served me well. Looking back, I think the experience sowed a seed because when I eventually came to manage the health board's suicide review process, interviewing and supporting relatives of the deceased was something I considered to be a privilege. I drew on a deep-seated skill set, forged on that icy path outside the rehab unit as a very junior psychiatrist. I didn't try to defend what had happened, instead trying to acknowledge their loss and anger. I was genuinely willing to review what had happened in a non-accusatory manner, to include any questions or concerns raised by the family. I wanted to learn from it and improve any aspects of care that might have been suboptimal, celebrate good practice and share the outcomes. If an angry relative hugged and thanked me after the process, or staff felt unburdened of some guilt, I felt they might all find some closure. If something good can come from a bad situation, then that is a positive thing.

Difficult conversations continued to present themselves in different settings. During my ward round, on two separate occasions, two patients requested private time together.

'We want to have a sexual relationship.'

My decision wasn't just based on human rights, equality, diversity, patient confidentiality or condom supplies. At the heart of my dilemma was the knowledge that here were two vulnerable adults, both with severe and enduring mental illness, who had personal and forensic histories that I could neither disclose nor ignore. Patients in the ward included a complicated mix of vulnerable individuals with drug-resistant major mental illness, among whom were victims of abuse, perpetrators of abuse and people who'd committed other types of illness-related offending. I couldn't share all of that, so they weren't necessarily going to understand my risk assessment and decision-making process. This consultant malarkey wasn't easy. They'd addressed the matter with me in a responsible, adult manner. If I agreed, I might knowingly be exposing a patient in my care to a risky situation. If I declined their request, they may resort to meeting in the bushes without using the appropriate protection. We agreed to a compromise of some time in their room to allow some privacy, but with the door open and no sexual relationship. I explained that I couldn't disclose patients' background histories, but this sort of thing could potentially be detrimental when there were fluctuating mental health issues. I also had to make sure that I wasn't setting a precedent. But there were no marriages or babies, thank goodness.

When asked to deliver some teaching on the psychiatric CPD (continuing professional development) programme and lunchtime learning for the whole hospital, I chose as my topic 'How to deal with difficult patients... and colleagues!' I suspect the majority of the audience wanted help with the latter. It went down very well. I got to share some of the nuggets of transactional analysis theory that I'd learnt as part of my own personal development. The idea that you can invite people to change their behaviour just by the way you interact with them is really empowering because people know that they can control themselves. When you're provided with a simple strategy to invite people to react differently, the belief that your awkward colleague is 'always like that, they'll never change' is shaken at its foundations. If they're in a critical parent position, they're inviting you into a helpless child position. Staff tended to relate to having felt bullied or belittled by a colleague and feeling powerless to respond. Noticing what's happening and not being drawn into that unhelpful, unhealthy transaction allows you to adopt an adult position, which invites them into an adult position too. It takes practice, but it works. I love it.

I also learnt a simple and effective way to give feedback in the moment. 'When you said X, I felt Y, and I would like you to do Z in future.' Letting the person know what they said or did helps to focus their learning. Sharing how you feel enlightens the individual about the impact of their behaviour. It's important to say 'I felt' and not 'You made me feel' because your reaction will be influenced by your own past experience and emotional baggage. They may not have intended to make you feel that way. Finally, by describing the alternative, you invite them to behave in a different way in future. If the feedback is delivered in a calm, factual manner, they're less likely to become defensive and will actually hear it, reflect on it and change.

I also enjoyed teaching and facilitating. When I'd completed the year-long Scottish Patient Safety National Fellowship programme, I asked if I could facilitate a simulation exercise with my peers. Despite some reluctance, the course organiser agreed. It was my take on an impactful simulation I'd attended as a new consultant, utilising and reinforcing some of my service redesign and patient safety learning. It was a hit. I had renal physicians, pharmacists, paediatric nurses, GPs, ENT (ear, nose and throat) surgeons and a microbiologist running around the room, role-playing being the chief executive and porters in the simulated hospital. I subsequently received invitations to facilitate the service improvement simulation with each new cohort of fellows. This was probably my favourite facilitating experience. I got to think in the moment, interact, facilitate, encourage participation in learning and read the room. Each simulation was different, with a variable outcome, depending on the choices made by the group.

To reinforce the learning points, it was rigged to work out every time. I felt so invigorated afterwards. It was like having my batteries recharged. How good would it be to have a job doing that every day? In the space of an hour, the cynics would see a 100 per cent improvement in quality and efficiency with the same resources. It was hard for them to remain cynical. Hopefully service improvement and redesign initiatives would be more likely to engage them in the future and reduce the likelihood of them becoming someone else's difficult colleague.

Chapter 32

Tales of the Heart

A re there any cases that really got to me and stuck in my mind? Yes, of course. One day, I was called to do an urgent psychiatric assessment for a murder case. I was really busy and tried to get out of it, but found out it was a woman from my patch who'd been charged with murdering her son. My antennae started twitching. It wasn't yet another alcohol-fuelled brawl gone wrong. This one sounded as if it might have a psychiatric component. I was asked to do a pre-trial report to establish if the woman was sane and fit to plead. It would be an opportunity for me to alert the court to any evidence of mental illness that may have contributed to the offending, as that would raise the possibility of a psychiatric defence. It would turn out to be one of the most impactful assessments I've ever carried out.

Over the years, I've always tried to be empathetic and listen non-judgementally to my patients, developing a degree of detachment from the emotions that may be triggered by a particular case. Here I was, a wife and mother, confronted by a young woman who'd killed her young son and cut out his heart, all as a result of a first-episode psychotic illness that had been missed. The case was reported in the press after the trial. She'd experienced religious hallucinations and delusions, believing she was on a mission from God and had been chosen to prepare for the second coming of Jesus. She believed her son would go to heaven, where she would eventually be reunited with him. If there are any sceptics out there who think that people feign illness to try to escape prosecution, they would've been convinced by this poor woman. She was so happy to have been chosen by God for the mission and so acutely psychotic that she had no idea she'd done anything wrong.

As her story unfolded, I became aware of my own acute sadness, experiencing an ache in my gut. Sometimes the influence of mental illness on offending can be blurred by intoxication, personality disorder and a history of antisocial behaviour that pre-dates the illness, but there were no such complicating factors here. She'd acted out because she lacked insight and had no idea that her experiences were symptoms of illness. To her, they were real. Her son was dead, she'd be spending a protracted period in a secure hospital, and she might never get to see her daughter again. It was beyond tragic. I spent several hours with her, trying to disentangle her psychotic symptoms. I wanted to hug her, but that was not my role. My job was to paint a detailed picture for the court of her mental state at the time of the offence, comment on her fitness to plead and her ability to instruct her lawyer, and identify if there was a risk to herself or others. My own emotions needed to be put to the side in order that I could do the best job for the court, and especially for the patient.

At some point, after treatment, when she regained insight, she'd need to process what had happened, make sense of it and come to terms with it. Capturing her story would play a part in that journey. I didn't see her as a child murderer. She was someone's wife, mother, daughter, who didn't ask to develop a mental illness. As I've always said, illness sometimes makes good people do bad things. It was my job to find them. An insanity plea was accepted by the court, and she was eventually admitted to a secure hospital. In the fullness of time, she will be considered for discharge for community rehabilitation and will no doubt require the services of a community forensic mental health service. An order will remain in place to ensure ongoing treatment, monitoring and engagement with services. Unfortunately, her main challenge will probably be overcoming public opinion and stigma.

When you have an illness, you need to treat it and learn to live with it. When you have a drug-resistant illness, and perhaps experience auditory hallucinations telling you to disembowel and decapitate, or you think people on the bus can read your thoughts, you need some pretty good distraction techniques. Everyone has to find a coping strategy that works for them. I had patients who found that being accompanied by their pet was a helpful distraction, or they put headphones on when they were outside. Some had less family support than others. However, even patients who do have family nearby can get into difficulty. One of my patients only engaged with our service after he attempted to murder his mother. Initial engagement with psychotic patients is often difficult; he had been no different. Multiple attempts to assess him had failed, both at clinic appointments and home visits. He went round to his mum's house and attempted to stab her. He wanted to stop her voice coming from the TV. She'd become involved in his delusional system.

As my management portfolio grew, I gradually reduced my inpatient commitment in the acute admission ward, intensive psychiatric care unit and low-secure ward. I then found myself having to negotiate with inpatient consultants when my community patients required admission. They weren't always forensic consultants, which meant our views about risk and how it should be managed didn't always concur. On one occasion a patient's behaviour had been settled in the ward, so time out had been agreed, despite ongoing paranoid delusions, auditory hallucinations and a recent history of psychotically driven offending. A clinical debate ensued, but my argument that psychotic patients shouldn't have access to named victims fell on deaf ears. As a forensic psychiatrist, I was the one with the most expertise in risk assessment and management, but was also in difficult territory. I was technically the boss. Colleagues often struggled to disentangle my clinician and manager roles. Managers attempting to interfere with a colleague's clinical decision-making – or worse, overturning their decision – do so at their peril. The long-term consequences can be catastrophic. In this particular situation, failure to act could also have been catastrophic for the patient, his potential named victim, my colleagues and our organisational reputation. I decided to seek a second opinion from an experienced forensic colleague outside our health board. I needed the decision to be viewed as a sound, clinically driven one, which it was, and not management interference. We moved the patient to the secure ward, and he was transferred to the care of the forensic team.

In cases of serious offending driven by major mental illness, the court often considers a compulsion order with restriction order (CORO) as the disposal because it means there will be multi-agency, public protection arrangements (MAPPA) put in place before any consideration of discharge from hospital. MAPPA will have input into the content of the proposed care and risk management plan, any changes to the care plan, monitoring arrangements in place, location of housing and so on. The patient will be compelled to take medication, attend appointments and live at an agreed address. This involves meetings between health, police, criminal justice, social work, prisons and the psychiatric advisor to the First Minister from the Scottish Government. After a lengthy hospital admission and a phased discharge to supported accommodation, with follow-up from the forensic team, it's so rewarding to see a young person overcome adversity and stigma, learn to live with their illness and start to rebuild their life.

CHAPTER 33

Conducting the Orchestra

When I became associate medical director for mental health in 2001, I was allocated a personal assistant. I remembered the advice of my consultant when I started as a higher trainee. He told me that picking your secretary is more important than picking your spouse because you spend a lot more time with them. I thought it was an odd thing to say, but I'd come to understand it. The relationship between a manager and their PA is complicated. It's an intensely personal experience, and rather odd in that the conductor of this orchestra is often absent from the pit. It's all the more interesting that the PA, as lead keyboard player, takes over the role of conductor in the boss's absence, and is often the wielder of the baton. That was how it was with Karen and me. I viewed her as my equal. We had different skill sets and were dependent on each other. In a hierarchical sense, I was the boss, but I was almost unable to function without her. It wasn't just her practical organisation of meetings, typing of reports and other administrative tasks, but her intuitive behaviour that mattered. There was an unspoken recognition that I was likely to forget the last-minute change of meeting venue, followed by the timely text reminder, the cup of tea for a stranger when I was held up in a meeting, and the printing-off of papers for the following week before she went on annual leave. In order to make this symbiotic relationship flourish, I was keen to ensure that I didn't play the status card. I respected Karen and I wanted her to know it.

'I know you're busy. Could you possibly prioritise one thing for me? I've put it on the top of the pile. The rest can wait.'

'No bother.'

I would often work late to complete a huge pile of admin, but by then her office would be shut. We developed a system: a Post-it note on her office door, saying 'The admin fairy has been. It's under the purple penguin.' This caused some puzzlement for anyone unfamiliar with our system. The purple penguin was a plastic secret Santa gift full of hand cream that I used as a paperweight. It identified her pile from the other piles on my desk, which had a 'to read' label. I never seemed to get to these piles. When I retired, they would be relabelled 'SHRED!'.

In terms of transactional analysis, I liked to think we were striving to respect each other, adult to adult, and avoid the parent-child or master-servant dynamic that's so often a feature of the relationship between boss and PA. When I had to leave work suddenly because Richard had unexpectedly been admitted to hospital, Karen was on annual Christmas leave. She left her house and went straight into work to put an out-of-office message on my email, answered urgent emails and cancelled all of my meetings. She was taking care of me and, with baton firmly in hand, was again conducting the orchestra. She didn't need instruction or my permission. She knew what to do and that I'd trust her to do it. When I was off, she sent me a text every day for three months, looking after my mental health, reassuring me that things at work were in hand, and allowing me to give my full attention to Richard.

Administrative staff like Karen often had to deal with

problems created by doctors, including trying to decipher their dictation tapes, handwriting and shorthand. As junior doctors, we were warned by the Defence Union to be careful about using abbreviations that could cause problems in court. The examples they gave included a doctor writing in notes that a patient had Harpic disease. When asked in court what this meant, the doctor had used it as a shorthand for 'clean round the bend'. Another doctor had written 'FLKNFF', and when asked in court what that stood for, they said it was 'funny-looking kid, normal for Fife'. Karen once had some difficulties with a temporary secretary. They'd typed a letter from my dictation tape and Karen decided to check it before passing it to me. The letter said that the patient had 'sexual dry f***ing'. Horrified, she looked at my handwritten notes to work out what had caused the problem. I'd actually written 'sexual dysfunction'. My clinical secretary Danna once encountered a problem with one of our nursing staff, who reported that she couldn't believe the length of someone's email address, which was given to her over the phone. When she recounted the conversation, it transpired that instead of writing the capital letters that the person was spelling out, she'd written the words tango, foxtrot, bravo, etc., thinking that these were actually words in the email address.

The more I became involved in medical management, the more I had to remind myself that I'd actually trained as a medical doctor. There seemed to be more and more corporate duties. Among these was having to attend the annual staff awards, with staff being nominated by colleagues and patients for a variety of categories. I nominated Karen for the Inspiration Award. She'd been an absolute rock, my right hand (and arm) for years. Nothing was ever too much bother; she was always smiling, and her work was always completed to an exceptional standard. There are people who make their mark on us as we journey through life. Karen is one of those generous, kind people I will never forget: a true gem. When I retired, I was careful to choose a gift that would capture the admiration and respect I had for her. I chose a heart-shaped Tiffany's necklace and earrings, as she'd left her handprint on my heart. I also named a star in the galaxy after her because in my eyes she's a star. I told her, 'It means you will still be looking down on me, keeping me right.' It was more than a relationship between a boss and their PA; it was a true friendship.

CHAPTER 34

Getting Hammered

I've always drifted towards leadership in a group setting. I'd describe myself as being a solution-focused ideas person who's keen to develop new opportunities and thrives in an ever-changing environment. I tend to be more of a starter and motivator rather than a finisher. I'm usually on to the next big thing, so it was fortunate that I also managed the service improvement team. During a leadership training course, I had a conversation with the GP cancer lead. Much to our amusement, we discovered that neither of us could read instruction manuals. I've never read an instruction manual in my life, whether it's for a computer, a vacuum cleaner or a Fitbit watch. I either have to push some buttons or ask someone to show me how something works. That's how my brain operates.

In the early days of my career, I used to illustrate my talks and presentations with acetates on an overhead projector. Those were the dark ages, pre-PowerPoint. They suited me well, as I got to use my artistic skills, making Mickey Mouse acetates. We had manic Mickey, depressed Mickey, drug-abusing Mickey and so on. For me, learning how to use an iPad was a major step forward. I could even answer emails and send an attachment, but you couldn't ask me to retrieve anything, cut and paste something or create a document. I put a red flag next to items I was finished with, and Karen would file them for me. When I retired, my successor inherited some pristine equipment, including a desktop computer, laptop and digital dictation machine. The iPad and smartphone at least had some wear and tear. I was told that the tapes and dictation machine were going to be condemned immediately after I left. I'm so old that I completed my entire medical degree at university without ever using a computer! My failure to be able to read and interpret instruction manuals has definitely hampered my ability to conquer technology, but with my personality and preferred learning styles, I have no desire to start reading manuals now. My drive and passion come from being free to generate new ideas and possibilities, living in the moment, interacting with others and feeling unconstrained. My glass is always half full, never half empty. Reading dry, boring text makes me feel as if someone has switched off my energy supply and I literally shut down and don't take anything in... a bit like the Duracell bunny, minus the batteries. My idea of an instruction manual would be a blank piece of paper ready to be filled with ideas.

This reminds me of a retirement dinner for a colleague of mine that was held at a small Italian restaurant. Our table was next to a couple of grandparents and their grandson, who was eating pizza. We'd bought our colleague a voucher for a chee-semaking course, as he'd told us he wanted to work in a cheese shop (yes, psychiatrists do listen). One of his colleagues was an excellent wood craftsman, so he'd made him a carved cheese board as a keepsake. After the retiree's heartfelt thank-you speech, his friend stood up and announced, 'There's more.' We looked on, unaware of what was coming next. He produced a wicker basket and emptied the contents onto the table. He put a cushion in front of the retiree, then placed a brick on top of it. Other random items appeared: a sock, a hammer and a

Dictaphone. With great ceremony, he placed the Dictaphone inside the sock, sat it on top of the brick and handed over the hammer, saying to my colleague, 'You're retiring. You'll never have to do dictation ever again. Go for it.' Admin had always been his least favourite part of the job. As he pulverised the Dictaphone, the crunch of plastic was muffled by the sock. Pizza boy's eyes popped out on stalks! It wasn't a typical retirement dinner, even for a psychiatrist. I laughed with my colleagues and thought, 'I know exactly how he feels!' There were times when I'd have happily pulverised a Dictaphone.

One thing all of my colleagues agreed on was that, when it came to technology, I was a dinosaur. It bordered on phobia, but I did have several compensatory coping mechanisms. Their names were Karen and Danna, and, if I needed anything done in a hurry at home, Richard and Fraser. When Karen and Danna were away, it was like functioning without one of my arms. The core of every team I've ever worked in has been the administrative staff. They can make it or break it. Regardless of the paper mountain, the number of items with 'urgent' written on the top or the deluge of emails I'd sent at midnight, they miraculously got on with the job at hand. I wouldn't have survived without them. I'm not against technology, I think it's great, and I advocated that we should use it to progress our service. I just couldn't get on with it myself.

I now know why I don't like technology. I completed the Myers-Briggs personality test on a leadership course and came out as an ENTP (extraversion, intuition, thinking, perception). ENTP personality types are described as individuals who gain energy through interactions with people and objects in the outside world and tend to be more abstract than concrete. They focus their attention on the big picture first, rather than the details, and on possibilities rather than realities. They tend to value objective criteria above personal preference, and when making decisions they place more weight on logic than social considerations. They also tend to withhold and delay important decisions, preferring to keep their options open should circumstances change. The ENTP person identifies complex interrelationships between ideas, people and things and is often quite entrepreneurial. They see possibilities all around them and get excited about these possibilities. This can make them charismatic, inspiring leaders who are catalysts for change.

I must add here that my experience with hammers wasn't restricted to pondering acting out my frustration with Dictaphones. After receiving intelligence that one of our patients was paranoid, depressed, using illicit drugs and had been threatening people, it was time for yet another friendly home visit from the forensic team. There was no answer when we knocked at the door, the grass was overgrown with weeds and the blinds were shut. We tried the door... and it was unlocked.

'Hi, it's Dr Morrison and one of the nurses; can we come in? You missed your appointment, so we've just popped round to see if you're OK.'

'Right.'

The room was dark, with dust motes illuminated by the light shining through a crack in the blinds. The patient was slouched in a chair, surrounded by discarded cans and plates caked with dried food. My eyes were drawn to the hammer on the coffee table, which was within easy reach. The fug that hung in the air caught my throat. Every surface had a dusty film of ash on it, which seemed to have spilled from the overflowing ashtray. I suppressed a gag. We needed to ask about the hammer, but conversation wasn't easy. He was so slurred and drowsy. We needed to establish if he was paranoid again, if he had a named victim in mind for the hammer, where he was getting the benzodiazepines (which he was clearly abusing), and whether, with his consent, we could remove the hammer. These situations were always delicate. He declined the offer of an inpatient detox, but thankfully we retrieved the hammer without incident.

CHAPTER 35

The Psychiatric Milliner

'm not a hat person. This probably dates back to my hatred of a green hat my mother insisted I wear to Sunday school when I was about eight years old. It was emerald green and looked a bit like half of a rugby ball, with a stalk sticking out of the top and wide flaps that came down over my ears and tied under my chin. It was the sort of hat that had never been in fashion and probably never will be. There was also an off-white bathing cap covered with large white floppy flowers, which I had to wear to swimming lessons at school. Then there was a purple skull cap covered in large purple daisies, which I wore when I was a bridesmaid. That's right up there as a hat never to be forgotten. I must confess that I probably picked that one, as it matched my flowery purple bridesmaid's dress. I've always liked things to match. Let's just say I've been traumatised by hats. Nowadays, I avoid hats because of hat hair.

However, my whole career has seemed to involve juggling different hats. My roles have included psychiatrist, clinical supervisor, educator, doctor, parental figure, manager, authority figure, expert witness, specialist, service improvement manager, innovator, adverse event reviewer, patient safety champion, disciplinarian, organiser, developer, spokesperson and complaint handler. To me, they're all facets of Rhona.

It was quite a task to keep track of the hat I was wearing at any given time as I usually wore several at once, depending on who I was talking to within the same group. I always knew which role I was playing with each person, but because the hats were invisible, others would sometimes attribute hats to me that I wasn't wearing. This could lead to complex inter-personal dynamics, even when I tried to establish from the outset what my role was. When I had to admit one of my community patients to the inpatient unit, there were crossed wires and assumptions about the clinical hats I was wearing. As a forensic psychiatrist working in the community, I was requesting clinical input for my outpatient from an inpatient consultant, i.e. a clinical peer. This was a doctor-to-doctor interaction, so the hat in my mind was clear. However, my colleague might have seen me as an authority figure, their boss, the person who'd disciplined them following a complaint, the one who'd redesigned their service or provided expert opinion about their patient for court. Contrary to all of this potential confusion, I was also the person expected to support those same staff through personal and emotional turmoil and give them time and space to refocus. It would sometimes become emotionally messy. I concluded that it would be easier to be a manager in a service where these other dynamics were not in play. My transactional analysis training was incredibly helpful in unpicking some of these dynamics, bolstered by my dim and distant memories of psychodynamic psychotherapy and the transference and countertransference that may have been at play.

One long-standing, occasionally challenging relationship with a colleague came full circle when they sent me an email just before I retired from clinical practice, saying, 'Do you know something? I'm going to miss you.' He'd heard I was planning to write a book and bought me *The Weekend Novelist* by Robert J. Ray and Bret Norris, which teaches you how to prepare, develop and write a novel. Starting to read that book actually got me started on my writing journey. A colleague from the forensic team then sent me a link about the Scottish Book Trust New Chapter Award for new Scottish writers over the age of 40. That's me, I thought, so I decided to start writing earlier than anticipated. I'm grateful to both because writing my memoir has been great fun and extremely cathartic.

So, here's some advice from the psychiatric milliner. Whenever you choose to wear a new hat, it's important not to look in the mirror and think that it suits you because how well it fits actually depends on how others view it. They'll attribute all sorts of personal meaning and history to the person in the hat: for example, a childhood experience of a difficult interaction with an authority figure may result in them assuming you'll be the same, interpreting intentions behind your actions that aren't there and making assumptions about how you'll react. This will influence how they'll view you in your new hat and the kind of reception you'll get. It can be a long journey, trying to get them to see you in your hat and not react to you as if you're someone else. When you're required to wear multiple hats, as I was, you'll require a fair amount of emotional intelligence to monitor what's going on in the moment and manage it.

Coaching training taught me to notice assumptions, challenge them, and monitor my own internal dialogue and physiological responses. This flexibility of response is something that has stood me in good stead throughout my career. It involves active listening, responding and reframing things for people when they've clearly misinterpreted the situation due to hats getting in the way. Perhaps the solution would've been to carry a hat stand with me and have a visible record of which hats were being worn at any given time. Why has no one thought of that before? I guess it wouldn't fit in the briefcase unless I had one like Mary Poppins. Emails always complicated these dynamics, as it was difficult to monitor assumptions, the emotional nuances of any conversation and the impact on the recipient. Perhaps a hat emoji would have helped? I can't believe the technophobe came up with that suggestion! It's only now that I've stopped to reflect on the hats, and I wouldn't have had it any other way. I get bored with the status quo and predictability. Changing hats multiple times throughout the day suited my personality type and kept me energised. It required dancing in the moment. Perhaps that's where Fraser gets his love of musical theatre. He's energised by putting on different costumes and performing different roles.

Wearing the hat marked 'member of the health board corporate management team' was both a privilege and burden, but it afforded me the opportunity to influence service development. My claim to fame must be securing £1 million for the development of mental health services during a recession. The woefully under-resourced Psychology and Child and Adolescent Mental Health Services (CAMHS), long waiting lists and government targets for waiting times definitely boosted my case. The personal price I paid was losing several years of my life to paperwork and meetings. My constant companion was Kathy, the general manager. We were polar opposites: she was introverted, reflective and measured; and I wasn't! Perhaps we were the yin and yang of the mental health management team, but we worked well together, respected each other's strengths and became friends. That was helpful, as being a medical manager doesn't win you too many consultant friends. I'd jumped ship and become 'one of them'. Despite that, I still believe you shouldn't complain about anything if you're not willing to become part of the solution.

CHAPTER 36

A Glass Half Full

My approach to life is a bit pick 'n' mix. I've taken pieces of knowledge, learning and experience and drawn upon them to inform how I function. Here's some advice I gave to my trainees, however senior: 'Sit in with as many colleagues as possible. Observe how they interact, how they ask questions and how they deal with sensitive issues. Take the best practice from all of them and amalgamate it to form the type of clinician you'd like to be.' Despite having been on many courses and collecting many certificates along the way, I wouldn't say that I'm an expert in any particular area, or can even describe the core of what I've learnt. All of these courses shaped my practice and how I related to other people. The list of credentials might sound impressive, but I never really practised in any of these specific areas. For example, I achieved an MBChB (Bachelor of Medicine and Surgery), MRCPsych (Member of the Royal College of Psychiatrists) and completed training in HCR-20 (risk assessment), PCLR (Psychopathy Checklist Revised), RSVP (Risk for Sexual Violence Protocol), solution-focused therapy, cognitive and behavioural skills for high-risk recidivists, business coaching, transactional analysis, the Scottish Patient Safety Programme fellowship and so on. But what did I actually learn?

1. Take a detailed history and include all of the questions that are risk factors for violence so, if present, you can monitor and manage them in future.
2. Try to view the world in a glass-half-full way, seeing the positives and the opportunities for improvement. Be open to the possibilities change can bring.
3. Avoid making assumptions and challenge any existing ones. They could inhibit you from finding solutions or result in misinterpreting the behaviour or intentions of others.
4. Don't ever think 'That's just how they are; they'll never change'. Work out the dynamic that feels stuck and change your behaviour, then invite the other person into a different way of interacting with you.
5. Risk assessment isn't something you complete to tick a box. It's a dynamic process that needs to be updated daily, based on the information available. Then the risk management plan needs to alter, to address the fluctuating risk. It's not something experts in risk do for you; it's everyone's business. It's how we keep ourselves, our patients and the public safe.
6. Small, incremental changes and improvements can accumulate to take us where we need to go. Patients should be encouraged to create small, achievable goals in order to achieve a better quality of life, rather than people viewing them or judging themselves as (for example) 'a homeless, schizophrenic paedophile with a heroin addiction'. We can support rehousing, treat the illness, work on the sexual fantasy and risk management plan with the paedophile, organise a methadone script and encourage prosocial behaviour. Underneath all of that, there's a person who may have been self-medicat-

ing with illicit drugs to cope with the illness and sexual preferences that they didn't choose to have. Chaotic behaviour linked to the substance misuse may have resulted in disinhibition, offending, financial problems and homelessness.

I guess 'jack of all trades, master of none' would sum up how I see myself at the end of my journey. I've seen most things, and nothing fazes me, but I couldn't quote you chapter and verse on the diagnostic criteria, research evidence base or the most up-to-date treatment for anything. Could I manage the person and the problem confidently, with empathy, in a person-centred, non-judgemental and facilitative way? Yes. In my experience, patients value dealing with a person who respects them as an individual and wants to help them with their situation and doesn't just quote all of the evidence without seeing the person behind the label. Bad behaviour or mental illness don't define a person.

Any great team consists of many component parts, and so it was with the forensic community mental health service. Each member brought a special ingredient to the mix to create a great recipe for success. I'd always inhabited the role of ideas person and motivator, encouraging the team to take on a wider remit, training to develop a new skill set, volunteering for the next opportunity and so on. My fair-skinned consultant colleague, the one at risk of post-traumatic stress regarding an incident with fake tan, pants and a sarong in Benidorm (that's another story), once told me, 'I feel terrible, I never come up with any good ideas for the team.' I confessed that I was constantly telling myself to 'Stick a sock in it, Rhona', but I just couldn't help myself. I think out loud, with thoughts forming as I speak, so if I don't keep talking, my thinking is halted. My thoughts tend to race, so trying to hold on to a good idea or find an opportune moment to share it never works because the ideas keep coming. It annoys me as much as it does everyone else! I reminded my colleague that my thoughts and 'good ideas' only work if someone more measured introduces some logical steps and suggests that we agree on the best idea, because we don't have the capacity to do everything. I'm fine with that. I've always been a 'first and only draft' sort of person, i.e. 'good enough', not 'gold standard'. I'm happy to share a good enough idea or plan and accept contributions from the team, to shape the idea into its final form. I can't understand people who do 39 drafts to make something perfect before they share it. It's usually a great piece of work, but they'll probably have missed the deadline for funding and may have alienated colleagues by presenting it as a fait accompli rather than engaging them in a collaborative effort.

Over the years I've learnt that the service changes that are sustained beyond the initial burst of enthusiasm are the ones where the ideas have come from the staff. They own the idea, it's their baby, they're invested in it and are therefore more likely to make a success of it. But it takes a bit more effort at the beginning. As an ideas person, I had to morph into a facilitator to achieve this. My general manager once suggested that I should develop my coaching skills as a way of helping others to generate ideas and solutions. Little did I know what an impact it would have on my practice. I enjoyed it so much that I followed up with a transactional analysis-based business coaching course and made two long-standing friends in the process, Liz and Loretta. We coached each other on everything... they know too much!

As the sort of person who was always keen to come up with ways to improve services, I was enthusiastic about exploring opportunities to expand my knowledge and expertise in service improvement methodology. It was no surprise, then, that I jumped at the chance to take part in the Scottish Patient Safety Programme. I was required to come up with a patient safety project, e.g. managing sepsis, managing left ventricular heart failure, preventing wound infection, etc. The general consensus is that patient care is safest when it's evidence based and consistent. Quality of care shouldn't be dependent on the specific expertise of the clinician on duty. If you carry out the process or procedure in the same, evidence-based way every time, then symptoms will be identified and treated consistently with a positive outcome. This often involves the creation of checklists, protocols and pathways. As a psychiatric manager and forensic psychiatrist, I wasn't so sure that identifying a project in my area would be that easy. What to choose? We were advised to pick something simple to try out the techniques we were being taught. I decided on something fairly ambitious, non-forensic, and not in my own clinical area, which would involve multiple agencies. I clearly fell at the first hurdle!

Locally, frequent attenders to A&E were sometimes referred to as psychiatric frequent fliers. Colleagues in the General Hospital were constantly complaining about the time that was taken up by repeatedly seeing the same people, and our colleagues in the police had the same complaint. They were often the ones to bring them up for assessment following yet another crisis in the community when they'd absconded from the local children's home, threatened self-harm after a fall-out with their boyfriend or tried to jump from a bridge. I decided to develop multi-agency risk management plans for frequent fliers. These would be shared with emergency services so that first responders would have 'need to know' background information and guidance on how to manage the case, as often the crises occurred out of hours when the regular care team wouldn't be around to give advice. We required patient consent and input to create and share the plans to make them as patient centred as possible. I borrowed the idea of incorporating a graded traffic-light risk management plan from MAPPA paperwork, used for high-risk forensic patients. The person-specific risk factors were laid out, with green, amber and red descriptions of how they may present at different levels of risk, alongside the graduated risk management steps required. There was also service-specific guidance – for example, advice for police on how best to interact with them. A simple example might be advice for male staff not to approach a patient from behind, as they'd be likely to feel threatened and it might trigger specific abuse memories. In the past, that had led to the patient running away from staff, being apprehended and then restrained by male staff, thus re-traumatising them.

Trying to introduce these new forms out of hours, when I wouldn't be there, wasn't going to be easy. We had to find a way of developing the multi-agency plans, flagging up the existence of the plan, agreeing where it would be held and how often it would need to be updated. We also had to accommodate multiple IT systems. The police system didn't allow data to be held on people who didn't have a criminal record. The police officer who was liaising with me took the issue as far as Scotland Yard, as they felt it was a good example of inter-agency collaboration and we needed a solution. The project was ambitious and only partly successful, but hopefully when it did work it made a positive impact on patient experience and safety. If nothing else, I'm hopeful that the development meetings raised awareness about the importance of holistic, multi-agency, person-centred care in mental health.

CHAPTER 37

From Russia with Love

Richard and I liked to travel. In the early days, when we had no money, it was a cottage in Wales and a bus trip to Austria. Later on, we took holidays abroad every year and an annual February trip to our snowy timeshare in Ballater in Aberdeenshire. We started cruising the year after 9/11 and never looked back. The idea of a long flight to Florida no longer seemed so appealing, especially as the 9/11 incident had brought family tragedy for me, with my cousin Mark having died in the South Tower of the World Trade Center. The kids loved cruising and so did we. It was the perfect way to see the world. We cruised every year after that, including trips to the Mediterranean, the Arabian Gulf, Mexico, Alaska and China, but our lodge in Royal Deeside was a much-loved constant, surrounded by snow, ice, beautiful Scottish scenery, river walks and a welcoming country club and spa. In the early days, Jill and Fraser had their first go on a dry ski slope, quad biking and pony trekking through snowy mountains and rivers.

Later in life, our love of cruising took us to the Baltic, this time without the kids. We went on to visit Norway, Sweden, Finland, Denmark, Russia, Germany and Estonia and had booked a variety of excursions. There was lunch on a horse farm, a trip to a concentration camp and a grand tour of St Petersburg. Before we left for our holiday, Richard noticed a nondescript rash on his shin and had been to the doctor. It soon spread to his other leg. A series of lotions, potions and antibiotics failed to resolve it and we noticed some swelling and a red flush to his skin, which looked a bit like cellulitis. It flared up when we were away. His legs became so swollen that, if you pressed down, it left a dent in his flesh about half an inch deep (pitting oedema). His calves were at least 50 per cent bigger than normal, with obvious fluid retention, and were swollen right up to his knees. He was feeling increasingly tired on the excursions, particularly in Russia and Germany, where we had booked full-day tours that involved a lot of walking and standing. He stayed at the drop-off point and told me to meet him back there when I finished the tour. Something was clearly wrong.

When we returned home from the cruise, I was determined to get to the bottom of the mystery rash and the pitting oedema. Eventually, after a multitude of tests, the echocardiogram showed an abnormality. Richard received a message to say he may have a heart murmur. I reassured him that this could be fixed. The fluid retention was probably being caused by a dodgy heart valve and a bit of heart failure. I agreed to attend his next GP appointment, but we didn't get the news we expected. He appeared to have cardiomyopathy. A series of blood tests, angiography, MRI scans, ECGs and genetic testing subsequently established that he had idiopathic, left ventricular dilated cardiomyopathy. It wasn't ischaemic heart disease; it was just one of those things that can happen. It had caused left ventricular heart failure as well as the rash. He was put on a vast array of tablets to improve his heart function but essentially he now had a lifelong condition. He felt tired a lot of the time and slept quite a bit. His walking was also restricted due to arthritis in his knee, so there'd be no more trips to

Russia or long cruise excursions. We kept on cruising, but had to choose more sedate options.

Shortly after his diagnosis, I nearly caused him to have a heart attack. His doctor had been asking the usual questions linked to heart failure.

'Do you get breathless on exercise or when you're climbing stairs?'

'No.'

I queried his response on our return home. He never did any exercise to find out! I suggested that we should check because it may affect the assessment and treatment options.

'Climb up and down the house stairs twice and then see how you feel.'

After exercising, he sat down on the couch and said he felt OK, but then went a bit grey.

'Are you OK?'

'I've got a dull feeling in my chest and a tingling in my left arm and hand.' He played it down, saying, 'I've had that before and I've never come to any harm.'

I couldn't believe he'd had these symptoms before and had failed to mention them. It was also a worrying development. I phoned NHS24 for advice about the exercise-induced chest pain radiating down his left arm. Their protocol suggested a blue light ambulance. The guilt was overwhelming. He was admitted for investigation, but with no beds available on the ward, he was put on a trolley in the corridor among drug users in handcuffs with police escorts. As there were no beds in cardiology, he was eventually taken up to a general medical ward. ECG and initial bloods were thankfully not suggestive of a heart attack. Two days into the admission and he still hadn't seen a cardiologist. His ECG recordings were being viewed remotely, but that's a poor substitute for a living, breathing expert opinion and some reassurance. Visitors weren't allowed during the day, but when I asked to speak to a doctor in the evening, no one who knew about his case was available. He was under the care of the receiving physician, who was an infectious diseases expert. I was worried and felt very frustrated. It was out of character, but I was so angry I ended up having a verbal altercation with a nurse and a junior doctor.

'The cardiologist used to visit the ward, but they retired. He'll be seen by a cardiologist when he's transferred to the cardiology ward.'

'When will that be?'

'No idea; they're full.'

I had a bit of a rant: 'It's not your fault that they don't have cardiology beds available, but the cardiologist has two legs and can come to us. This is totally unacceptable.'

Next day, there was still no cardiologist. I decided to intervene by contacting the medical director, who I knew really well because he was previously the medical director in my own health board. I explained the scenario and said I was really unhappy. Could he help? Within 20 minutes of his sympathetic listening and reassurance, I got a call from Richard.

'There's a very angry-looking doctor, I assume a cardiologist, walking towards my bed.'

My intervention had worked. It shouldn't have to be like that, but there are a few perks of working in the health service.

Then Richard discovered he had diabetes. He'd been experiencing dry mouth, excessive thirst and was going to the bathroom several times a night. He linked his dry mouth to a recent dental procedure, but I insisted on blood checks for diabetes. The results came through when we were riding on a steam train over the famous Harry Potter viaduct up in the Highlands. His blood glucose was really high, and an urgent GP appointment was recommended. He never did get to grips with how to manage his diet, but took his medication religiously. We decided to take a trip to Florida that summer. On the first day we arrived, we arranged to go to SeaWorld to have a dolphin trainer experience. We'd been in the park for about two hours, standing under an umbrella in the shade, talking to the trainer, watching the dolphins do tricks, when Richard said, 'I don't feel well. I need a seat.' There were no seats. I watched as he turned grey and slid down the wall onto the ground, unconscious. We were panic stricken. Knowledge of his cardiomyopathy and history of heart failure automatically led us to the assumption that he was having some kind of cardiac event.

'Wake up, Richard.'

No response. The trainer radioed for the paramedic staff at the park's medical centre. Richard started to regain consciousness, but seemed confused.

'I want to go to sleep...'

He started to drift off again. Jill was screaming at him to stay awake. We tried to sit him up and thought we should try to get some fluid and sugar into him, as he was diabetic and probably dehydrated too, due to the extreme heat. A passer-by offered a lemonade slush puppy. We tried to spoon some into his mouth, but it just poured down his chin. I had a bad feeling about this. Is this it? Is he going to die in America? What will we do? I was catastrophising. Back in the medical centre, his blood pressure and temperature were checked. He was hypotensive but appeared to be more alert in the cool environment and managed to drink some water. Over the next few hours, he gradually improved and drank more fluids. Eventually we were allowed to leave. The conclusion: overheating and dehydration.

'We'll be hiring an electric mobility scooter in every park. That's non-negotiable!'

We thought we were going to lose him right there at the dolphin pool. He was too young to be saying goodbye, but it was a reality check for everyone and a reminder that we needed to respect the cardiomyopathy and adjust our expectations in terms of physical exercise. The next day, we received the dreaded phone call from home, which inevitably meant something had happened to one of the grannies. Richard's mum had collapsed at home. We felt helpless on the other side of the Atlantic and guilty for not being there. Our first port of call on return was the nursing home where she'd been temporarily admitted. My impression was a stroke with super-imposed delirium, but she hadn't had any investigations. After a quiet word, she was transferred to hospital. Unfortunately, she never regained her previous level of functioning. This once proud lady had a slow, painful decline over many months. She soon required full-time care, and Richard's sister Louisa selflessly moved back home to cover the nights until her death in June 2017.

CHAPTER 38

Your Baby's an Adolescent

I embarked on my career in psychiatry in 1986, always knowing that a perk for psychiatrists (at the time) was that we could retire on full pension at 55. Fast forward to 2017, and I'd started to mentally prepare for my retirement in March 2018. This significant ending in my life was going to be a two-step process. First, I would go part time, giving up my clinical practice; second, I would retire from my management role seven months later. As a result, I received gifts and retirement cards from patients and said goodbye to them, but continued to work in the service as the manager and had the potential to bump into them in my other role. The same could be said for my clinical team colleagues. I had such mixed emotions. While I was eager to start my next chapter, I was ready to give up being on call, court reports, urgent home visits and arguments with colleagues regarding clinical care. But I was sad to leave behind colleagues I'd worked with since the early Nineties as they'd become part of my family. Jill made one of her signature 3D frames for the team office. It said, 'We are all MAD here... MAD = Making A Difference.' That summed up exactly what we were all about.

My decision to go part time that August allowed me to plan for how I would fill my time once I'd thrown off the shackles of the NHS. I'd come full circle and, having achieved all I'd wanted to achieve, I felt ready for my retirement with Richard. The plan was to take lots of holidays, pursue new hobbies, write a book, get back to my painting and take up some sport again. The six stones I'd lost on the Cambridge Diet two years previously had been whittled down to three by the constant nibbling of chunky KitKats and the odd curry. Time for a diet!

Coming to the end of my clinical practice was a significant juncture; a time for reflection on what I'd achieved in my career and what impact, if any, I'd had. I realised that I'd occupied a parental role not just for my two children, but for some of my clinical team and patients as well. On one forensic team awayday, the team manager said, 'The forensic team was your baby, but now it's an adolescent and you have to let it go.' How impactful! I felt quite emotional. He was absolutely right. We'd been talking about changes in the team, a new direction and the potential impact of a change in my managerial role. I felt as if I was abandoning them, but it was really happening. 'Mum' was leaving the building.

Individual staff said how sad they would be to see me go and how much I'd been the backbone of the team for them. Many had known me since they were young nurses and trainees in other locations and had been taught or supervised by me for years. Kirsty, Sheila, Joan and Willie had all worked with me elsewhere and applied to work with me when I started the team, which was quite a compliment. John completed the starting line-up of nurses. Whenever a list went up for a night out, a 'bring and share' lunch, a task to be completed, or an action note for a meeting, everyone was referred to by their first name, except me. For years I referred to myself as Rhona and told staff to call me that, but I was almost always called 'Dr M'. Other consultants and staff came and went and were referred to by their first names. When I asked why, they just told me it was a mark of respect. That was how it was, and I had to live with it. In contrast, some of the patients who'd known me for years called me Rhona. That felt odd too as it breached what was usually a helpful boundary, required when I had to challenge them or detain them under the Mental Health Act.

In forensic services, patients were often with the team for years. When I was at the point of departure, it highlighted just how dependent some of the patients had become, both on me and the team. Some had been supported for more than 20 years, through good times and bad, births, deaths, marriages, illness, imprisonment, drug relapse, guardianship hearings, suicide attempts, new jobs, relationships... we'd been there with them. We supported them to develop independent living skills, learn emotional coping strategies and socially integrate as we cheered them on their recovery journey. Many of them still had limited family support and by default had come to see us as their family. A degree of dependence had inevitably developed.

We once helped a young couple arrange their wedding and argued for another patient to gain custody of his niece, then supported him as he took on his role as a parental figure. We were there with our patients through radical cancer surgery, court cases, threats of drive-by shootings, supervised access visits with estranged children, hospital admissions, miscarriages, bereavement, relationship failures, drug relapses, and also for all of their successes. They were living with illness and didn't let it define their future. One patient wrote me a truly moving letter when I retired, talking about how I'd supported him over the years, especially when his mother died, and how he'd viewed me like a 'second mother'. He pledged not to let me down. Having an effect on even one patient along the way makes it all worthwhile. Another patient made me a gift when I left, with her initials embroidered in the corner.

'This is so you don't forget me, Dr Morrison.'

It's still on my desk. I've been on a personal journey with a small group of patients over the span of my career, often seeing them more often than my own family. I'll definitely not forget them. I've learnt so much from them. I have so much respect for them and how they've coped with such disabling illnesses, and yet they've risen above it all and lived their lives.

Some of them met me in prison, in the intensive psychiatric care unit, in the low-secure forensic ward or in the forensic community mental health service, and many have been in almost all of those settings at one point or another. There are also those patients who were probably glad to see the back of me – a small group who saw me as the doctor who detained them and made them take the horrible medicine. Most had a psychotic illness and lacked insight, so I was perhaps never going to win them over. They may have believed they had extrasensory perception, that the government was interfering with their TV or that I was involved with a paedophile ring; I believed they were delusional and in need of treatment. Others were troubled by distressing command hallucinations, believed there were demons entering their house via the toilet (and stuffed clothes down the toilet to block them out), dismantled electrical equipment because they were convinced that cameras had been hidden by their neighbours or tried to hang themselves to escape the stress of messages on the radio. Those patients may have struggled more with the challenge and change when I retired. For some, when families and friends came and went, nurses changed and social workers moved on, I was the constant in their lives. For them, my retirement was like a bereavement. Change can be a good thing, but it needs to be managed. The nurses and psychologists were brilliant in helping patients prepare for the change, framing it as a positive, but also acknowledging their loss. I'm certain that some colleagues were glad to see me leave, but I guess that's inevitable, especially for a medical manager.

The team was well established and had turned into something I was proud of. Like a relay race, it felt important to hand the baton on to someone I trusted, to look after my 17-year-old baby. It was like vetting your child's girlfriend or boyfriend. Laura, an excellent trainee, would be 'cooked' a few months before my retirement. I decided that if I went part time for a while, I could create a job for her to apply for before I left. There was no guarantee she'd get it because it was an open advertisement and I wouldn't be on the interview panel, but it felt right to at least create the opportunity. My family would be in safe hands. She got the job, and it allowed for a smooth handover, with joint clinics to introduce the patients to my replacement. They weren't being abandoned; they were moving on to someone I trusted and had trained. It felt good. Change would bring fresh perspectives and a more up-to-date approach. The team had grown over the years and the majority of the new team members were also former trainee doctors, nurses and psychologists who had returned to the fold. The team was about to enter its next phase.

Leaving the team proved to be emotionally challenging. I decided to treat everyone to one last night out, a family dinner. Presents didn't seem to be appropriate. What could I buy that would actually express how I felt about this team of truly wonderful, talented individuals? They were all unique and special. You can't buy that. I wrote an ode to them called *The Essence of Forensic*, within which I tried to capture all the characters in the team, their valued contribution and some of the stand-out moments of our journey together. I read it out, amid tears, before I said my final goodbye. It finished with...

Each of you have played your part,
leaving a handprint on my heart.
It was once my baby, but now it's grown up,
To my adolescent team, I say bye and good luck.

As one of my gifts, the staff gave me a beautiful Mont Blanc pen, which was to be used to sign my memoir, once published.

At least someone had faith that I'd eventually get it written. There were also flowers and balloons, but the most memorable gift had to be the retirement cake. I lifted the lid to reveal a box full of very interesting cupcakes. The toppings were all different and included reminders of specific incidents and characters along the way. There was a bottle of Diet Irn-Bru and a chunky KitKat as a reminder of my lunches on the go; a machete and handcuffs; and even one with my face on it – but the piece de resistance was the cupcake with the male genitals on top, reminding me of my scrape in outpatients all those years ago. Not many people can say they had a retirement cake sporting male genitals! They told me I'd have to wait until March 2018 for the other part of my gift. I was intrigued.

As my retirement date was fast approaching, I was invited to attend the annual long service awards to receive my badge for 30 years of service. I was also asked to make a short video about myself and my career, picking as a backdrop somewhere that might be interesting for me to talk about. It was either going to be a police station, a court or a prison. Cornton Vale was in the frame: the umbilical cord was pulling me back again. Standing outside the prison, our mini film crew (me, the cameraman and the interviewer) were approached by an irate operations manager, in prison uniform, demanding that we remove ourselves from the premises. He assumed we were from the media and making some sort of critical documentary. It wouldn't be the first. We explained that we'd sought permission and it was for an internal staff awards celebration, but that didn't seem to work. We were unceremoniously dumped out onto the street, where we continued to film with the prison as the backdrop, dodging cars and lorries when necessary.

This experience triggered a reflection on my whole career. Looking back, I'm full of admiration for the resilience of the people who became part of the forensic family, who overcame the stigma of their diagnosis and offending, and learnt to live with their illness. Suicide is a recognised outcome for a small group of patients, but I was fortunate to have very few incidents of suicide in my own patient caseload. My inner voice was my constant companion. I listened to my patients and what mattered to them, but if the situation felt unsafe, I exited. 'Trust your gut' is an old-fashioned saying, but it's so true. I often experienced something physical and unspoken inside of me, a sort of common-sense moral compass that always helped to steer me along the right path.

CHAPTER 39

Will We Land the Plane?

On a Mediterranean cruise in the summer of 2017, I noticed that Richard was quite lethargic and off his food. He'd been subdued and had spent a disproportionate amount of time on the couch before we left. I put it down to the impact of dealing with his mum's protracted illness and eventual death the previous June. She hadn't been eating or communicating and, because there was no blood supply to her foot, the flesh had rotted away. We could actually see bones and tendons in her ankle, and she needed morphine. She'd wanted to die at home, and the family had respected her wishes, but it had taken its toll on everyone. It wasn't easy to witness her demise. I remember saying, 'I don't want to die that way.'

That September, Richard and I took Jill on a surprise city break to Prague for her 26th birthday. When he tried to get out of bed on the first morning, he was nauseated and dizzy and couldn't stand. His symptoms suggested acute labyrinthitis, one of the few things I remembered from medical school. He spent the rest of the weekend in bed while Jill and I tried to make the most of the break, constantly checking in on

Richard. Getting him home on the plane was a challenge, but his symptoms had subsided a little. The GP told us that labyrinthitis can last up to six weeks and we should just ride it out. I was now the chauffeur, as he couldn't drive due to dizziness. He found this really difficult, as driving was his passion.

As the weeks passed, I was starting to notice warning signs that this might be more than labyrinthitis. My medical doctor's antennae, which had lain dormant for most of my career, were twitching. He was lethargic, lacked motivation, had lost his appetite for several months, and had nausea and balance issues. Then he started having trouble finding the right words and experiencing memory lapses. He even forgot our postcode and his bank PIN number. The red warning light was flashing again. This didn't fit with labyrinthitis. I thought he might have something organic going on in his head.

We revisited the GP and she decided that an ENT referral was now warranted (there was a 26-week wait on the NHS). The week before, I'd carried out a consultant appraisal interview for the professor of neurology. I took advantage of our friendship and asked him for advice to see if I was totally neurotic in wanting Richard to have a neurology examination and CT scan. He said no, I wasn't neurotic, and agreed with me. However, the GP didn't see the need for a referral to neurology, as nothing had shown up when she'd examined Richard. We decided to go private, to get him seen and scanned as soon as possible, and went with the professor's recommendation of a colleague from Edinburgh. He couldn't find any focal neurological signs either, and said he thought the balance problems were possibly ENT related after all. However, he did check Richard's memory for me and noted some subtle abnormalities. He said a scan may help to identify evidence of an early organic process such as dementia. He was incredibly thorough and dealt with this delicate subject very professionally. We felt listened to.

A week later, on 16 December 2017, we went to the hospital in Edinburgh for Richard's CT scan. The children had wanted to come, but I'd reassured them that it wouldn't be reported that day. The consultant had agreed to look at the results promptly and contact us before Christmas so that we wouldn't be waiting and worrying unnecessarily. I got the impression that he wasn't expecting to find anything, and it was perhaps more of a reassurance for me as a fellow doctor. Having helped Richard into his gown, I sat in the tiny changing cubicle. By then, he couldn't balance to dress himself. I was told he'd only be about 20 minutes. A while later, a member of staff came out to reassure me: 'Richard's fine, but there'll be a delay. We've decided to do a contrast scan as well.' I went on high alert again, suspecting they'd found some sort of abnormality. At this point, I was still thinking about dementia and, if I'm honest, somewhat selfishly thinking 'What does this mean for me?' They brought Richard back a short while later and I helped him dress. He couldn't bend to put on his socks and shoes or stand without feeling a 'whoosh' in his head, feeling unsteady and then falling to the side. The staff returned.

'Can you please wait? The radiologist is on the phone discussing the scan with Richard's consultant. He isn't in the hospital today. Can you take Richard up to the ward in a wheelchair? The senior registrar will have a word with you instead.'

If you pared back the niceties, the message was that the scan had revealed three lesions, and the main one was near the cerebellum (the centre of the brain, which coordinates motor activity). Richard had a brain tumour. Because he'd had a bit of a headache and been vomiting over the past two days, they were worried that the main lesion may be blocking the flow of cerebrospinal fluid around the brain. They'd be admitting him directly to the ward. We'd moved seamlessly from private CT scan to inpatient NHS care. We were both shell-shocked. My thoughts were racing. 'Oh my god... brain tumour, more than one. Are these secondary tumours? Does he have cancer somewhere else in his body? What does this mean in terms of prognosis? What will I tell the kids?'

On cue, Jill phoned my mobile. I made the decision not to answer. I was upset, tearful and in shock, but it was crystal clear to me that news like this should be delivered face to face. On the one hand, I knew both kids would panic when they didn't get a response; but on the other, I hoped it might alert them to the fact that there was something wrong and prepare them for it. I decided to text them and ask if they and Richard's sister could meet at our house, and I'd come back to update them, as Dad had been admitted to hospital. They suggested driving over to the hospital to meet me, which made much more sense. I told them I wanted to speak to them in the car before they went up to see Dad. They were now well aware that something serious was on the agenda. There's no guidance on how to tell your kids that their father has multiple brain tumours. Obviously everyone was distraught and there were lots of questions about tumour type, treatment options and likely prognosis, which I was unable to answer. There were more tears when they went up to see their dad. The most amazing thing was just how stoic Richard became. He demonstrated a stable, calm acceptance in a sea of emotion and uncertainty.

The next few days were dizzying: discussions regarding a possible biopsy, debulking of the tumour, likely tumour type and treatment options, CT and MRI scans to confirm that the tumour was confined to the brain and not secondary to cancer elsewhere, and plans to transfer Richard to the neurosurgi-cal unit in Glasgow. It seemed odd and disappointing that the consultant we'd seen privately didn't visit Richard in Edinburgh. It seemed out of character, as he'd come across as the sort who'd be likely to pop in on his way home. As he'd told us that he didn't think there was anything major going on neurologi-cally, I suspected he might be feeling quite bad. Some weeks later, all was explained when we discovered he'd had his own family tragedy on exactly the same day.

After a few false starts, Richard was eventually transferred to the Queen Elizabeth University neurosurgical hospital in Glasgow. He was put under the care of a charismatic Irish neurosurgeon called Mr O'Kane, whom we had Googled and watched as he operated on someone who was awake for the operation. He'd also been featured on the BBC programme *Scotland's Super Hospital*. Richard had been in hospital for more than two weeks before he actually got to meet Mr O'Kane, but it was worth the wait. He shook our hands warmly then jumped up on the bed to talk to us. He'd reviewed all the scans and was proposing either a biopsy of the lesion in the ventricular wall, or in the cerebellum. One was marginally less invasive, but may not yield a sample; and one involved removing part of Richard's skull and fiddling around in his cerebellum and brainstem. The list of potentially serious neurological complications was long. Richard was to be prepared for theatre a couple of days later. We told everyone about the planned neurosurgery and the risks involved. Due to his cardiomyopathy, I raised concerns about the potential risk of an anaesthetic, and so, on the day of surgery, I was called in to talk to the doctors. Mr O'Kane was back and had brought the consultant anaesthetist with him. The anaesthetist was concerned about Richard's cardiomy-opathy and calculated that the risk of him not surviving the operation was one in five.

'Richard, your body is like an aeroplane and you're the pilot,' said Mr O'Kane. 'I have the equivalent of remote controls and can tinker with the plane, but if it crashes and burns, I will walk away, and you won't.'

We liked his analogy. It was straightforward and refreshingly honest.

'I won't do anything unless you want me to, but I'm on the journey with you and I'm willing to have a go, despite the anaesthetist's reservations. The anaesthetist laughed me out of court due to the risk. I've a reputation for taking on cases and surgeries that others might not.'

We were left to consider what we wanted to do. Any surgery

would not be curative; it would simply be to take a biopsy to try to identify the tumour type and inform any treatment options. According to the scans and Richard's odd symptom profile, all of the surgeons thought he had a rare primary CNS lymphoma (blood cancer localised in the brain), which can affect the whole brain function, although you only see lesions in some places on the scan. If the biopsy showed such a lymphoma, he wouldn't be eligible for chemotherapy, as it required a huge intravenous fluid load that his heart wouldn't survive. Tests on the ward revealed that his heart was now only working at 35 per cent of its normal function.

Richard asked, 'What's the prognosis without the chemo?'

'It's weeks or months, Richard, not years,' said Mr O'Kane. 'We'll prescribe a course of high-dose steroids, which you can tolerate, and that will alleviate symptoms for a while.'

We thanked Mr O'Kane and the other doctors for being so open and honest with us. The message was terrifying but clear. They'd answered all of our questions, which allowed us to make an informed decision. We were both in agreement that quality of life rather than quantity was more important to us, and we saw little benefit and more risk if we went ahead with the general anaesthetic and biopsy option. We opted for steroids only. I had the job of relaying our decision to the family. Louisa struggled to take it in and wanted to explore the small-print research options. I think it was a form of denial. I agreed to ask the surgeon about it, and he confirmed that Richard wasn't a candidate. I was keen for everyone to accept the new reality so that we could make plans and start to prepare ourselves for what was ahead. Richard remained philosophical: 'I know what's going to happen, but I don't know when. There's no point in getting upset; I can't change it.'

He felt cheated. Despite being a non-smoker and non-drinker, he wasn't going to be around to enjoy his retirement. He reflected on the fact that both of our fathers had found themselves in the same situation. It was then that I started to grieve for the future I wouldn't have with Richard and prepare for one without him. It was a surreal time. I like to be in control, but this was way beyond my control. The way I deal with emotions is a bit like letting the fizz out of a bottle a little at a time, so it doesn't explode everywhere. I get a bit tearful, have a wobble, and minutes later I'm back to being in control again. I don't dissolve in a heap or keep it all bottled up inside either. Ultimately, it's better out than in. Richard was using the same strategy and together we appeared to be coping well in the circumstances.

He was discharged in mid-January after a month in hospital. His mobility was going to be a challenge. He'd tried to walk to the nurses' station with his Zimmer frame for the Hogmanay bells, but had fallen over and hit his head. We also had some difficult conversations about finances as Richard became preoccupied with leaving his affairs in order. That was something he could control. Fraser and Louisa waded through papers, drawers and filing cabinets, trying to find the documents that were preoccupying him on a daily basis. As the tumour progressed and he started taking steroids, I observed a change in his personality and behaviour. My once feisty husband, the Mount Vernon moaner, mellowed, grateful for the help of the doctors and nurses. He couldn't thank them enough. He gradually became more dependent and childlike, but appreciated what everyone was doing to help him. I gradually morphed into a full-time carer and didn't begrudge one second of it. I didn't return to work, and we wouldn't be going on our big retirement cruise to the Far East with our best friends, Alison and Derek. Alison has been my friend since university and has always been a source of great comfort and support. It helps when your best friend is a psychotherapist. Our friends would be making trips to visit us instead. Morag, our friend who introduced us to the wonders of our favourite Ballater timeshare, flew up from England to say her goodbyes, knowing she'd be back all too soon when Richard's journey came to an end. It meant a lot to us both.

When my mum visited, she chose to sit at the end of the couch, nearest to the large riser recliner chair that now supported Richard. I remembered the time, after she'd had major heart surgery, that I'd decided to cross the divide between handshakes and hugs. Her phrenic nerve had been damaged during surgery and her diaphragm wasn't functioning properly, so she'd been put back on a ventilator. She almost died. I needed to hug her, but it felt awkward and outside of our normal relationship. But it was the right thing to do, and I suspect we both needed it. Thankfully, she did recover. So, it was touching to watch as she crossed her reserved barrier with Richard. She put out her hand and held his, something she hadn't done in 38 years of knowing him. She simply left it there, maintaining contact with him as they spoke. That single act of closeness and intimacy showed the emotion she was unable to articulate. She was about to lose her son-in-law and her daughter was going to be a widow.

CHAPTER 40

The Beginning of the End

The forensic team's surprise four-day 'weekend away' treat to mark my retirement in early March 2018 had been planned long before Richard had become unwell, and I'd had to leave work prematurely. It was a girls' trip to a lodge with a hot tub, caviar and champagne. I really needed this, but wasn't sure I was going to make it. Jill stepped up to support her dad and Fraser to allow me to have a farewell celebration with my team. It was so lovely to have some respite from my caring role for a few hours. They gave me space, but made me laugh. I'd hardly been out of the house for two months and there hadn't been much to laugh about. They'd made photo books that captured some of our team antics over the years. It was a lovely memento. At this welcome retreat, I enjoyed some unconditional friendship and a brief escape before the inevitable end point in my journey with Richard. It meant so much that colleagues like Karen, Aileen and Clare, who had left the team, came back for our reunion and my NHS finale. Our newest recruits, Katie, Clare and Laura, were now settled in and part of the motley crew too.

I lost more of Richard in the ensuing weeks, little by little, faculty by faculty. We both knew what was ahead, but not the timescale nor the detail of how it would end. Because of where the main lesion was located, I'd prepared myself for the tumour blocking off the flow of cerebrospinal fluid around the brain. That would mean headaches, nausea and loss of function. I'd studied neuroanatomy as a trainee doctor, but didn't want to intellectualise this very emotional and personal journey by reading up on it. The haemato-oncologists (blood cancer specialists) had said, 'Something catastrophic will happen and you'll know it's time. We can't say what it'll be because the tumour is affecting Richard's whole brain.' It was daunting and scary information to process.

Just as storm clouds may signal the approach of a nasty weather front, we'd had our own warning signs. Richard couldn't get out of the chair without assistance and couldn't walk without his Zimmer frame and me bear-hugging him from behind, as he would list to one side and fall over. He needed the stairlift to get upstairs to bed, a wheelchair to get to appointments, his speech was slower and more slurred, and he'd developed double vision (now wearing an eye patch to cut out stimuli from one eye). He'd also had sickness and headaches the week before, with resulting left-sided facial weakness, and was generally more placid and dependent on me. He needed help to get in and out of the shower, to get washed, dried and dressed, and I had to help him in the toilet. He was also becoming distressed by occasional incontinence. I helped him to eat, and he drank out of a beaker with a straw. Despite all of this, he was still able to give me a cuddle and enjoy the company of friends and family. He kept saying, 'I'm sorry, you shouldn't have to be doing this.' He also made some random, impatient demands, such as, 'I want Russian caramels.' Jill would be sent off to source them. I don't think he even knew what a Russian caramel was! I desperately wanted to do all of the caring myself, even though I used to see myself as someone who wasn't wired for this type of care. I'd always told my mum that if she got to the stage of needing care, I'd happily pay for it, but couldn't do it myself. Not very daughterly, I know, but I was just being honest. You can never really predict how you'll react until you actually find yourself in this situation. I told Richard, 'I promise to look after you at home, but if they can't control the pain, you'll need to go to the hospice. I don't want you to suffer like your mum. I won't let that happen to you.'

My retirement tea at the health board took place three days before my actual retirement date, which would be on my birthday, 23rd March. Richard was deteriorating fast, but insisted that I go. It was nice that so many people turned up to wish me well, but the most touching thing was a video message from a colleague who couldn't attend. He summed up my career perfectly, even my habit of consuming Irn-Bru, a chunky KitKat and egg mayo sandwiches for lunch every day, and the difficult job I had trying to manage consultants, which was like herding cats. And he was one of them! Meow... I also received lots of spa vouchers for when it was all over.

The following night, Richard woke up with a headache and felt nauseated. The medication didn't help. I pulled him up to a sitting position. As I let go of his arm he slumped to the side, back onto the bed, unable to maintain his body posture. I pulled him back up, initially thinking he was just tired, but when I pulled him up to standing and placed his hands on the banister, his legs gave way under his 21-stone bulk, and I was bearing most of his weight on my shoulder. I screamed for Fraser. Together we supported Richard on his way back to bed, but his legs wouldn't hold him, and we had to sit him on a dining room chair midway between the en-suite toilet and the bed. At that moment I realised he wouldn't be getting out of bed again. This was it; this was the catastrophic change we'd been warned about. Here it was, in the glow from the light in the en-suite, the approaching end of our 38 years together.

'Richard, you need to stay in bed now. I'll call the hospice and district nursing staff. We need help to manage your symptoms and keep you at home.'

I spoke to the staff at the hospice and told them Richard had deteriorated and needed stronger painkillers and anti-sickness medication. Meanwhile, Richard wanted to go downstairs on the stairlift. I had to tell him it wasn't safe to move him out of the bed: 'I think this is what they warned us would happen.'

At 2.30 am, I called Jill.

'It's time to come home. Dad has deteriorated quite a bit. I don't think it's going to be long now. I think it's time.'

In the morning, I called the hospice.

'I need help. I want to do this right, at home.'

The hospice-at-home team – two fresh-faced, smiling staff – arrived within the hour. In that instant, I knew we'd cope. I'd been up for most of the night so was dispatched downstairs for tea and a rest.

'Richard, we'll give you a bed bath. Would you like a shave?'

'Yes.'

'Would you like a massage?'

'No.'

'A massage might relax you.'

He finally agreed.

'I'll give you a nice wee foot massage.'

I told the hospice team that, in the 38 years I'd known him, Richard had always demanded that I stay clear of his tickly feet. I went downstairs and relaxed, knowing he was in good hands. I trusted them with my precious Richard. Upstairs, I could hear them talking to him and having a bit of playful banter. He was still able to engage to a limited degree. Eventually it all went quiet, so I went back upstairs.

'How did you get on?'

'He loved it. He fell asleep during the massage.'

He was settled now, asleep, bathed, clean shaven and his hair combed. We were going to be able to do this. There had been four callouts in 24 hours for the district nurses to come and administer morphine. Now the hospice team had arranged for a morphine pump, steroids and anti-emetic (anti-sickness) medication. I knew that if they got the doses right, he'd be pain free, the nausea would subside, and he'd sleep. It would inevitably suppress his breathing and he was likely to drift away from us. I just needed to be beside him. I told the family and our friends that we were in the final stages. Even on the pumps, he was still able to hear and respond. Lynn, my childhood friend of more than 50 years, visited and delivered the bombshell that husband Gillies had resigned from his job, realising that he was unhappy teaching, and that life was too short. This was partly in reaction to what had happened to Richard, and Richard seemed pleased. As the evening progressed, we took turns going up to sit with him, but he slept a lot. We had an ongoing dialogue with the nurses, and they reassured us that the on-call team was aware of the situation and would respond if necessary. I had to sign a DNR form (do not resuscitate), which had been discussed earlier on with the GP. These are not easy conversations for staff or families to have, but in Richard's case I had no hesitation. This part was easy. He no longer had quality of life.

Chapter 41

23.3.18

Jill was now staying with us.

'Let's go to bed. I'll wake you up if there's any change, I promise.'

'Night night, Mumsie. Night night, Dad.'

I cuddled into Richard, as close as I could get without dislodging the morphine pump in his leg. He was sleeping peacefully, propped up on his pillow.

'Night night, Richard. I love you.'

No response.

I woke suddenly at 4.30 am, aware that something was wrong. Slightly disoriented, I could hear Richard's laboured breathing. It had a phlegmy rattle, which reminded me of the very sick patients I used to see as a junior doctor all those years ago in the Southern General.

'Richie, you're OK; I'm with you.'

As I kissed his cheek, a tear landed on his nose. No response. I woke Jill and Fraser.

'I think it's time.'

I didn't need to say anything else. We had lost Gran Morrison less than a year before. Jill's only other encounter with death was a traumatic one, having found an 18-year-old prisoner hanging in his cell and having had to cut him down. Fraser had never had to deal with such a situation. They looked on in disbelief, trying to process what was happening in front of them. There were silent tears.

'Fraser, can you call Auntie Louisa? Tell her it's time to come over. Dad's breathing is very laboured now.'

It meant a lot that all of us were there with Richard at the end. The nurses had brought little pink sponges on sticks to swab his mouth when he couldn't drink. We used them to clear his mouth. He was still with us, but not responding. Occasionally we thought he nodded slightly as if he could hear us. Perhaps that was what we wanted to believe, desperately willing him to stay with us. I cleared thick, brown, sticky material from his mouth. Where was it coming from? Louisa was silent at first, in tears of disbelief. She wasn't ready to cope with losing her big brother so soon after her mum. She kissed Richard, and Fraser provided a much-needed hug. I lay in bed with Richard, as close as I could, as these were going to be the final cuddles. Louisa was distressed by the noise of his rattling breathing.

'Let's move him up the bed, he's struggling.'

'No. He's comfortable, he's not in pain, he's sleeping. Leave him. It's time to let him go.'

I asked for a few moments alone with Richard. This was it, my final opportunity to tell him what he needed to hear. I kept it short.

'I love you, Richie. I'll always love you. We've had a great 38 years together, more than most people. No one can take them away from us. We've made such great memories together and have two lovely children to be proud of. Now it's time to let go and be with your mum and dad. It's OK, I love you.'

He didn't respond, but I cuddled hard, kissed him again and again and hoped he could hear me. Then I told everyone they could come back up.

'Mum, it's after midnight. It's your birthday,' said Jill. 'I think you should open the present that Dad got for you.' The unspoken words were 'while he's still alive'.

She handed me a beautifully wrapped rectangular box. I was secretly hoping it was some sort of keepsake because I was going to need one very soon. Inside I found the perfect gift: a beautiful Raymond Weil watch with a mother-of-pearl face and small diamonds set into it where the numbers should be. It was a reminder of our time together. I cried happy tears because he'd done so well, and sad tears because he wouldn't live to see me wear it.

Then Jill said, 'Mum, I think we should play the CD Fraser made for Dad.'

At his dad's request, three days earlier, Fraser had recorded three songs for the funeral in a professional recording studio. Richard was so proud of Fraser's talent and musical theatre achievements and would cry at the end of his performances. Fraser had played the CD for his dad just after he'd made it, in a private boys' meeting. Richard's speech was slurred by the end, but he said, 'I like it, deep voice, play it on Friday.' Richard had wanted to share it with family and friends at my joint birthday and retirement get-together. We all hoped that Richard could hear it as we played it to him again in the bedroom. I kissed his cheek. The words were so poignant. I reached out and held Richard's hand. It felt cool.

Jill said, 'Mum, Dad's hand is grey; he's getting cold.'

His face was still warm when I kissed him, but his body was starting to shut down his peripheral circulation. It was getting close now. His breathing was becoming shallower.

'His breathing is still strong; I don't think it's time,' said Louisa.

I'd been trying to prepare her and the kids for weeks, as Richard was losing more and more function on a daily basis, but Louisa wasn't ready to believe it. His face was pale and cool now.

Richard slipped away at 7.45 am on my 55th birthday. No

more phlegmy rattle. Silence. We were all there. I cleared his mouth with another sponge and kissed his cheek. I couldn't hold back the tears now.

'I love you, Richie.'

'I love you, Dad.'

'I can't believe it. Oh Dad, Dad.'

We sat with him for what seemed like an age, just to make sure he didn't take another breath. I felt for a faint pulse, but there was nothing. This really was it: the end of our journey together.

'Let's take a moment on our own to say our goodbyes to Dad.'

He was now a greyish white colour and cool to the touch. I needed to kiss his cheek one last time, and revisit a while later to repeat the process. Letting go wasn't easy but we'd managed his final journey well, with no regrets. We'd kept our promise to keep him at home, pain free, until he died. We'd had the chance to say what we wanted to say to each other. Not everyone is lucky enough to be afforded that opportunity. As endings go, it was a good one.

When I came downstairs to call the district nurse, the hospice staff and the undertaker, it seemed as if I'd entered a parallel universe. It was full of brightly coloured flower arrangements, retirement cards, get-well cards and enormous balloons. We'd had so many visitors and I'd had my retirement tea at work a few days before, so the house looked like a florist. It was my birthday as well as my official NHS retirement date and everyone knew it. Jill buys balloons at every opportunity, and this was a big opportunity. There were two huge silver balloons surrounded by tiny ones, saying 'Happy 55th Birthday' and 'Happy Retirement'. The postman arrived with another pile of cards, followed by an Interflora van with four flower arrangements for my birthday and retirement. There was one special arrangement of beautiful white flowers and dark green foliage in a large glass goldfish bowl. It was from Richard and had arrived a few hours after he'd passed away, while his body was still in bed upstairs. The district nurses arrived and certified his death. They stayed to give him a wash, which I thought was sensitive of them. They'd supported him in life, and now in death. I really appreciated that. I went upstairs for a final kiss and goodbye. He was cold and his skin felt waxy, with the mottled appearance that appears after death. I probably shouldn't have gone in that one last time, as it's an image that has stuck with me ever since, but I had to thank him and tell him I loved him one more time.

We were in limbo, not quite knowing what to do other than make some phone calls.

'He's gone. He passed away at 7.45 am.'

'Yes, we were all with him. He's at peace; he had no pain, and he died at home just like I promised.'

The undertaker arrived just after lunch. He sat on a large leather footstool flanked by the two large balloons, several flower arrangements and rows of birthday cards. I felt the need for an explanation, for fear that he was interpreting this to be a rather inappropriate party to celebrate my husband's death.

'It's my birthday. I retired from the NHS today. I know it looks odd to have balloons when my husband has just died. He weighs 21 stone. We have two stairs in our bedroom and there's a stairlift to negotiate on the way down.'

It's strange, the things you worry about at times of tragedy.

'I suggest you all wait in the kitchen, away from the stairs and the window until we have safely removed Richard to the ambulance.'

Perhaps I have a warped sense of humour or the black humour of a medic, or I've developed a coping strategy that fits with my glass-half-full mentality. I often remember sad days by linking them with a smile: my hurdles practice in the lilac shell suit when Dad died; and now the undertaker and the balloons. I see endings as new beginnings: chapters of my life that I've valued and learnt from but have now come to an end. I was about to start a new chapter, holding my memories close as I tried my best to move on with a positive attitude. Richard taught me about love, trust, reliability and honesty. He embodied my core values, and they live on in me, Jill and Fraser. I miss him. He was my rock. I fell off a cliff on 23.3.18. I lost my husband, my career and the future we'd planned together, all on the same day. My future will be very different to the one I'd anticipated, but it doesn't have to be a bad one. It will simply be the next chapter.

I'd spent my whole career saying 'I don't talk to dead bodies.' I can see the irony that, on the last day of my career, that was the only thing I wanted to do.

Postscript

Richard's funeral was a celebration of his life, shared with the hundreds of friends, family and colleagues who attended. His cousins had flown in from Shetland and the USA. His mum was a twin and the two families had been raised together. Standing in the church vestibule after the service, I shook hands and hugged the queue of well-wishers who offered their condolences. And then I saw him... I couldn't believe it. William, my best friend from university, now an eye surgeon in Blackpool, had come along to make sure I was OK. We'd only seen each other twice in 30 years since leaving university, but the bond created around the anatomy table with Albert had remained strong, and I felt so comforted in his embrace. This time, with the benefit of technology, we'd keep in touch.

A few weeks later, in the hope of rekindling my long-lost passion and starting to build a social network, I decided to join a watercolour art class. I'd missed the previous week's session, and had joined an acrylics class as a catch-up. I didn't know anyone there. I was sitting with my back to the door when the silence was broken by a latecomer.

'Hi, I'm Anna, sorry I'm late.'

The hairs on the back of my neck stood to attention. I

would've recognised the sing-song voice of that Lancashire farmer's daughter anywhere. It was my Anna, another of Albert's crew.

'Anna!'

'Rhona!'

We couldn't believe it, and just kept hugging each other. She'd known Richard all the way through university and was genuinely upset to hear about his death. Then she made a phone call to Angus, the kilted Scotsman (her husband).

'Angus, guess who I've just met... the lovely Rhona. Get the barbecue on; she's coming for tea.'

It was non-negotiable. My anatomy buddy was going to be taking care of me.

I loved painting so much that I went on to build a studio and start my own art business, Rhona Morrison Art. The next chapter was starting to take shape. A year later, on our wedding anniversary, I'd arranged to scatter some of Richard's ashes at the crematorium beside his parents. That morning, I had a business meeting at a cafe in Linlithgow and accidentally left some art prints next to the till while I was paying the bill. I called back to collect them after I'd been to the crematorium. The lady at the till complimented me on my paintings and asked if I had a website. I gave her my Rhona Morrison Art business card. She looked at me, stared at the card, then looked at me again.

'You're Rhona Pollock, aren't you?'

That wasn't on the card! I nodded, confused.

'I was a trainee nurse on your ward when you were a junior doctor at the Southern General. You were nice to me.'

How on earth did she recognise me and remember my name after all that time?

'I married Keith. You trained together. He works with your GP friend Catherine.'

I'm not a superstitious person, but surely it was more than a coincidence that yet another one of Albert's crew had mysteriously popped back into my life. Later that evening, after checking out my website, Keith's wife contacted me to buy my original painting of the Swilken Bridge at the Old Course at St Andrew's Golf Club. She said that, as Keith had proposed to her there, he would cherish the painting, especially as I'd painted it. At this point it probably wouldn't have surprised me if Albert himself had knocked on my door!

Looking back at my journey, I seem to have come full circle. Because of Vivienne, I wanted to help vulnerable people, and I'm proud to have achieved that. My legacy lives on in the staff that I trained, the services I developed, and in the patients who've gone on to live their lives to the full, despite their illness. I always wanted to pursue a career in art and, 40 years on, I'm doing that too, hopefully putting a smile on the faces of my customers in the process. It's never too late to pursue your dreams. As the song says, it's the circle of life that moves us through despair and hope.

Acknowledgements

This book would not have been possible without all of the wonderful people who have supported me, taught me, and kept me sane along my life's journey. To my family, thanks for putting up with me. I know I can be challenging. To my friends (you know who you are), thank you for your unwavering support through all of the ups and downs. A special mention for Alison, Lynn, Morag, Liz, Loretta, William and Anna – you know too much! My third baby, the forensic team – what would I have done without all of you fabulous people? You were the lifeblood of my career. I won't forget you. There have been many colleagues along the way who have shaped me, but a special mention goes to my long-suffering general manager Kathy and PA Karen, who were the voices of reason during the stormy management years. What was this journey about? It was about the patients. Thank you for allowing me to walk alongside you on your journey. I was inspired every day by your resilience.

This book finally came to fruition with the support and encouragement of Michael Heppell in the Write That Book Masterclass. He introduced me to Sue Richardson and Paul East from The Right Book Company, and then I worked with the wonderfully talented Beverley Glick, who introduced this technophobe to Google documents and guided me through the final editing. I also want to thank Ian Housley from Dormdust Productions who produced the audiobook.

Dr Rhona Morrison is a retired forensic psychiatrist who worked in the NHS for 32 years. Born and bred in Scotland into a working-class family, she has a grounded approach to life, with a generous helping of humour. She learnt the importance of being non-judgemental and supportive through her relationship with her sensory impaired sister, who had learning and physical disabilities. This prepared her well for working with mentally disordered offenders in custody and in the community, where she often felt humbled by their resilience and privileged to be part of their journey. As a passionate advocate of the destigmatisation of mental illness, she hopes her writing can shine a light on this specialist area of practice, so often impacted by negative attitudes and damaging assumptions.